PLAY THERAPY WITH KIDS & CANINES:

Benefits for Children's Developmental and Psychosocial Health

Risë VanFleet

Professional Resource Press
Sarasota, Florida

Published by
Professional Resource Press
(An imprint of Professional Resource Exchange, Inc.)
Post Office Box 3197
Sarasota, FL 34230-3197

Printed in the United States of America

Copyright © 2008
by Professional Resource Exchange, Inc.

This publication is sold with the understanding that the publisher is not engaged in rendering professional services. If legal, psychological, medical, accounting, or other expert advice or assistance is sought or required, the reader should seek the services of a competent professional.

The copy editor for this book was David Anson, the managing editor was Debbie Fink, and the production coordinator was Laurie Girsch.

Library of Congress Cataloging-in-Publication Data

VanFleet, Risë, 1953-
   Play therapy with kids & canines : benefits for children's developmental and psychosocial health / Risë VanFleet.
      p. cm.
   Includes bibliographical references.
   ISBN-13: 978-1-56887-112-7 (alk. paper)
   ISBN-10: 1-56887-112-0 (alk. paper)
   1. Play therapy. 2. Dogs--Therapeutic use. I. Title.
RJ505.P6V364 2008
618.92'891653--dc22

                                                            2008005600

DEDICATION

This book is dedicated to . . .

all those who work to improve the well-being of animals,

all those who help distressed children and families,

my uncle, Frederic Boerner, with his very special way with animals, including Poochie the dog, Charlie the crow, and Geronimo the bull,

my parents, Robert and Frieda VanFleet, who instilled in me love and respect for the natural world as well as for family companion animals, and

my husband, Mark Zarichansky, who patiently cares for our current crew of four dogs and two cats while I am often on the road for speaking engagements.

ACKNOWLEDGMENTS

I deeply appreciate the many people who assisted with the development of this monograph. The materials have been drawn from several diverse fields, and I was fortunate to have the cooperation of numerous professionals who freely offered their time, ideas, emails, article reprints, and encouragement. Their work has influenced much of my thinking, and I have cited it throughout the manuscript. I am also indebted to the participants in my "pets in play therapy" study who shared their time, information, and ideas with me.

This monograph would not have existed had it not been for Pat McCann, who runs the Border Collie rescue from which I obtained my play therapy dog, Kirrie. Without her dedicated work in rescuing dogs who might otherwise be euthanized, Kirrie might not have lived to enrich the lives of many children, as well as my own. Pat was the first to recognize the special characteristics that Kirrie has since used so effectively in her play therapy work. I am also grateful for my veterinarians, Dr. Kathy Purcell, Dr. Karen Pittelli, Dr. Olivia Charles, and all the people- and dog-friendly staff at the Boiling Springs Animal Hospital who take such good care of our four dogs and two cats. I have learned a great deal about animals from them, and Dr. Purcell suggested excellent reference materials for this project.

Previous drafts of the manuscript were reviewed by Judy Dawley, Gayle Kohr, Colleen Pelar, Mary Thompson, Cindy Sniscak, Frieda VanFleet, and Debra Vredenburg. Their helpful suggestions contributed much to the final version, and I am very grateful for their input.

Once again, I have appreciated the collaborative working relationship with publisher and editor Dr. Lawrence Ritt, managing editor Debbie Fink, production coordinator Laurie Girsch, and the staff of Professional Resource Press. They enthusiastically embraced this project and helped in countless ways to bring it to completion.

I am grateful for the children and families who have participated in canine-assisted play therapy with me through the Playful Pooch Program. I have learned so much from them, and they have taught me things that just are not written in any books. They have all contributed to this monograph in many important ways.

SERIES PREFACE

As a publisher of books, multimedia materials, and continuing education programs, the Professional Resource Press strives to provide clinical and forensic professionals with highly applied resources that can be used to enhance skills and expand practical knowledge.

All of the titles in the Practitioner's Resource Series are designed to provide important new information on topics of vital concern to psychologists, clinical social workers, counselors, psychiatrists, and other clinical and forensic professionals.

Although the focus and content of each title in this series will be quite different, there will be notable similarities:

1. Each title in the series will address a timely topic of critical importance.
2. The target audience for each title will be practicing professionals. Our authors were chosen for their ability to provide concrete "how-to-do-it" guidance to colleagues who are trying to increase their competence in dealing with complex problems.
3. The information provided in these titles will represent "state-of-the-art" information and techniques derived from both experience and empirical research. Each of these guidebooks will include references and resources for those who wish to pursue more advanced study of the discussed topics.
4. The authors will provide case studies, specific recommendations, and the types of "nitty-gritty" details that practitioners need before they can incorporate new concepts and procedures into their offices.

We feel that one of the unique assets of Professional Resource Press is that all of our editorial decisions are made by practitioners. The publisher, all editorial consultants, and all reviewers are practitioners and academic scientist-practitioners.

If there are other topics you would like to see addressed in this series, please let me know.

Lawrence G. Ritt, Publisher

PREFACE

I have not been alone in writing this book. The acknowledgments include some of the many human colleagues, friends, and family members who helped generously. But these people were not the only ones who contributed to the completion of the manuscript. Nearly all of it was written with four dogs – three Beagles and a Border Collie mix you will meet later in this book – at my feet and by my side. When I moved from my desk to my library to consult reference materials, four canines moved with me. When I returned to the keyboard, they wandered back to their sleeping spots nearby. My writing was interspersed with no fewer than 500 ball games, a small price to pay for the inspiration and companionship that these dogs gave me. Although the two cats showed considerably less interest in my creative process, they nevertheless provided entertainment and comic relief when they did appear.

I know that my interest in this topic arises from personal experiences with pets and animals I have encountered throughout my life. From Ivy, a cat that was with me for the first 19 years of my life, through an assortment of other family dogs and cats, to my current six animal companions, I have experienced our emotional interplay and attachment in ways that were enjoyable, touching, and just plain fun. While I recovered from donating a kidney to my brother over a decade ago, my pet dog at the time never left my side until I stopped moaning and groaning. She buffered my crankiness (I do not do well in the "patient" role) and provided a distraction.

As an amateur nature and wildlife photographer, I have had the unique opportunity to watch and photograph bears, sea otters, mountain goats, whales, birds, deer, elk, seals, and a whole host of other animals in the wild. A professional photographer from Switzerland I encountered on a mountainside during my first trip to Alaska many years ago taught me that if I sat still and had patience, Dall sheep ewes and lambs high up in the rocky outcroppings would approach me. I was rewarded for a half hour of stillness (a new experience for me) by 10 ewes and lambs whose curiosity drew them within 8 feet of me. My photography and wilderness interests have also given me sideline seats at extraordinary scenes of polar bears and Alaskan coastal bears at play.

I have also been fortunate to be involved with working dogs performing some of their traditional roles although these experiences were mostly for my enjoyment rather than out of necessity. I have helped train German Shepherd dogs for law enforcement use, and I have participated with Border Collies herding sheep in Scotland and the United States. My deepest involvement has been while independently mushing teams of six Alaskan huskies through the interior Alaskan wilderness (with a more experienced guide up ahead to rescue me should I get into trouble), and it has been during these experiences that I have realized how much true teamwork is possible between humans and animals.

My experiences with domestic animals, working animals, farm animals, and wild animals have enriched my life and taught me things I really needed to learn, and it was fun learning it. Because of these connections and experiences with the natural world, I have always suspected that animals have much to offer the therapeutic process. We are, of course, animals ourselves, but we have become estranged from the beautiful world around us. Learning and playing with our companion animals helps us grow and feel part of the larger environment.

Some still argue that animals do not have feelings and cannot really attach to us, but neuroscience, biology, veterinary science, medicine, and psychosocial research are showing this view to be incorrect. While people do sometimes project their own feelings and motives onto animals excessively, it is fast becoming clear that animals do have emotions and socially bonded relationships, and they are quite capable of interacting with us on those dimensions.

I once met an Alaskan brown bear while hiking alone through a thickly wooded area. I had been making noise in case of such an encounter, and my voice startled her. She was just coming out of the woods onto the trail, and we were only 15 feet apart. She had a cub behind her. She huffed at me, and I immediately averted my eyes, knowing that direct eye contact was a sign of aggression and that her huffing was a sign of her anxiety. I talked softly to her and walked slowly away, watching her with my peripheral vision. She came out of the woods, stood face to face with her cub, and swung her head periodically in my direction until I was 100 yards away. She then turned and walked in the opposite direction with her cub behind her. I realized that we had both experienced the same feeling – anxiety – in the unexpected encounter. Neither of us felt safe at that moment, and she was focused on ensuring that her cub did not tangle with this intruder. We both read each other's intentions as best we could, and although there were some tense moments, we eventually understood that there was no threat and went our separate ways. For me, this encounter illustrated the commonality of our basic emotions with other species, and the ways that our ability to read and understand each other's signaled intentions ensured our own well-being. Later I saw this same sow playing with her cub for an hour in the waters of the lake and wondered if she felt the same simple pleasures that I feel when playing with my grandchildren.

This monograph starts with a story about my play therapy dog and her ability to connect with other species through play, followed by a rationale for the use of animals, and particularly dogs, in play therapy. A great deal of fascinating and relevant information is available from interdisciplinary studies of the human-animal bond, neuroscience and animal emotions, and animal play. Due to space limitations, only an overview of this information is included here, but key references are provided and are well worth reading. The monograph briefly summarizes the fields of animal-assisted therapy and play therapy and includes excellent resources for further exploration of these fields. There is no intention to duplicate information that is available in the other resources cited. The bulk of the monograph describes the rationale, guiding principles, practical ideas and methods, and the potential benefits for integrating play therapy and animal-assisted therapy, with a focus on the use of canines for a wide range of child problems.

Most of this monograph is written for child and family clinicians who wish to use their own dogs in their play therapy work. Sometimes therapy dog handlers who are not therapists work collaboratively with play therapists, and this material can easily be adapted to that approach as well. Proper training and full understanding of the fields of animal-assisted therapy and play therapy are essential for the safety and well-being of the children, animals, and adults involved and for the quality of intervention.

Throughout the monograph, case examples are presented in smaller typeface and indented, and they are based on my experiences and those of other play therapists I know. Readers may not be able to use all of the suggestions, as dogs have different personalities and capabilities. The key is to develop interventions drawn from the unique characteristics, strengths, and needs of both the therapy dog and the child clients, and the cases provide examples of that. In all examples provided, identifying information has been changed to protect the privacy of children and families. At times, composites of several children or families are used, but the examples represent realistic descriptions of canines in play therapy.

The integration of play therapy and canine-assisted therapy is relatively new, and more developments can be expected in the near future. Certainly more research is needed. A handful of studies are underway, and more are planned. I am happy to discuss research ideas and methods with anyone interested in contributing to the field in this manner.

With all that said, I hope you find this work of interest and that it will facilitate dialog as theory, research, and practice in canine-assisted play therapy evolve.

Risë VanFleet
Boiling Springs, Pennsylvania
January, 2008

TABLE OF CONTENTS

PRACTICAL MANAGEMENT *(Cont'd)*

THE FIRST MEETING:
PREPARATIONS AND INTRODUCTIONS   50

CANINE COTHERAPISTS
IN NONDIRECTIVE AND
DIRECTIVE PLAY THERAPY   55

PLAY THERAPY WITH KIDS & CANINES:

Benefits for Children's Developmental and Psychosocial Health

THE STORY OF A
PLAY THERAPY DOG

Tippy Cat was just 6 months old when he showed up on our property nearly starved to death. As we fed him, he came closer to the house and eventually moved into our mudroom on cold nights and during the winter. Our relationship with him was mostly functional. He would tolerate us as long as we took care of his basic survival needs. He would avoid physical contact, and he quickly ran away from other people. The extreme neglect from his early life seemed to interfere with his ability to bond with us. Even when another stray cat, Bart, decided to live with us, Tippy Cat tolerated him but avoided most interactions. Although he did not seem afraid of our two Beagle dogs, Tippy Cat had little to do with them. I jokingly told colleagues that Tippy had an attachment disorder.

After 6 years like this, Kirrie, a rescued mixed breed dog (Border Collie and Beagle), joined the family. She had the energy and persistence typical of Border Collies and the happy-go-lucky temperament of Beagles. She was exceptionally playful. One day, the usually quiet Tippy was heard yowling from a room adjacent to where I was working. I assumed that Kirrie was pestering him to play and prepared to go stop the dog. To my surprise, the scene yielded something quite unexpected. Kirrie was taking the play bow posture and then bouncing around the room. Tippy watched Kirrie for a while and then chased the dog, eventually retreating to a safe place under a chair. The cat reached out a paw to swipe playfully at the dog, and the cycle was repeated. With Kirrie's persistent play invitations, Tippy Cat initiated the chasing play. I watched, photographed, and videotaped the play for about 20 minutes. This was the first I had ever seen Tippy Cat play.

Immediately thereafter, Tippy Cat jumped into Kirrie's chair and curled up to sleep. Kirrie, who outweighed the cat by at least 35 pounds, carefully stepped onto the chair and curled up behind the cat. The cat nuzzled the dog and they slept together in the "spoon position" for nearly half an hour. This play-then-nap-together cycle became a daily event for Kirrie and Tippy. Within 2 weeks, Tippy Cat was spending more time in our family room, playing with Kirrie, rubbing against people's legs, and eventually spending brief periods in our laps. Nearly 3 years later, Tippy Cat and Kirrie play together most days, and their play times are still followed by a nap together. Whenever I go outside to play ball with Kirrie, Tippy invariably appears within 5 minutes to watch the game. He watches everything that Kirrie does and frequently initiates expansive outdoor chase games with Kirrie at dusk.

As I watched this remarkable and sudden transformation of our reticent cat, I strongly suspected that the cross-species play had much to do with it. The play had seemed to facilitate an attachment – between the dog and the cat, and eventually between the cat and the humans in the family. It was then that I began to think more seriously about training and using Kirrie as a play therapy dog, and about the potential for such work with traumatized and attachment-disrupted children.

For 2 decades prior to this event, I had periodically used animals in a variety of ways in conjunction with play therapy. Of course, I had animal miniatures and puppets in my playroom since the start of my play therapy work. As an avid nature photographer specializing in Alaskan wildlife, I had some of my photographs of Alaskan brown bears, Dall sheep, and sea otters on the walls of my office and playroom. My inclusion of animals seemed natural enough, given children's great interest in them, but I had never used live animals for great lengths of time or in particularly systematic ways. In fact, I felt a bit sheepish about involving the animals, as somewhere in my professional development I had gotten the impression that this would be an inappropriate way to conduct therapy.

It was children's interest in my pets that prompted me to include the animals in the first place. I had an office and playroom that adjoined our house, and the pets were usually outdoors when I saw clients. On rainy days, however, the dogs were kept in the kitchen where they usually stayed quiet during play sessions or parent meetings. Children and adolescents frequently asked if they could meet the dogs. With their parents' permission and under my supervision, I let the children give cookies to the dogs, pet them, and even taught the children a few commands and tricks that the dogs knew. The children never failed to ask about the dogs or request a short playtime with the dogs once they had met them.

My black cat, Bart, became involved in a different way. He had been named for the marvelous children's therapy book about trauma, *Brave Bart* (Sheppard & Manikoff, 1998), mostly because he was completely black like the story's main character. His personality more resembled that of Bart Simpson, but I took his photograph sitting with the *Brave Bart* book, and we gave it to children and adolescents in our practice who had loved and benefited from the book. A 6-year-old girl asked to meet the Bart in the photo, and she often played with him while I met with her parents in an adjacent room where we could still watch the pair of them for safety purposes. The child had originally come with her parents for Filial Therapy sessions after she was traumatized by her father's military deployment immediately after the 9/11 attacks. Filial Therapy worked well to alleviate the family's distress, and they quickly shifted to home play sessions and discharge from therapy. Her parents told me later that when her father was deployed to dangerous regions of the world for a second time, she told them that she needed to "go see Bart again." Around the same time, a reticent and oppositional 18-year-old girl who resented being referred to therapy by her parents, asked to hold Bart during a session. Bart, who is a very social cat, seemed delighted and curled up in her lap for the entire hour, purring contentedly and stretching as she petted him. The girl dropped nearly all of her defenses and began telling me her feelings about a number of difficult situations in her past and current life.

Until the playful relationship between Kirrie and Tippy Cat altered my thinking, I had only considered using animals as an adjunct to therapy – a brief transitional interlude as families were departing. After I had completed a considerable amount of training with Kirrie, I began using her more systematically within play therapy sessions. I began reading more and attending seminars on the human-animal bond, animal play, aversive-free dog training, and animal-assisted therapy. Kirrie's first clients were foster children with long histories of challenging behaviors. Although the children typically did well with play therapy and Filial Therapy, their histories of abuse and neglect, coupled with frequent and unexpected moves within the foster care system, often made the attachment process difficult, with many setbacks. Their responses to Kirrie were dramatic. The foster parents saw it, too. I knew that something was happening that was more than a momentary experience.

I broadened my use of the dog and began an exploratory research project on the use of animals in play therapy. I immersed myself in the literature and had conversations with play therapists, animal behaviorists, positive dog trainers, animal-assisted therapists, veterinarians, biologists, educators, canine search-and-rescue handlers, and animal lovers. I tried new ideas of my own. I found a remarkable multidisciplinary group of people with similar interests and fascinating experiences. I discovered that there was a great deal of conceptual, empirical, and pragmatic literature available as I wandered into fields beyond my own.

This monograph is meant to share what I have learned so far and to open new fields of inquiry and practice that hold tremendous potential. The integration of animal-assisted therapy and play therapy seems a natural blend of two potent approaches, both with solid theoretical and expanding empirical bases. More multidisciplinary dialog and study is needed, and it promises to yield innovative ways of helping children and families. It could also assist the current human alienation from the natural world and promote kinder, more understanding relationships between the human and nonhuman animals that populate it.

Because this monograph is written primarily with mental health therapists in mind, I have not included much background information about the psychosocial problems that children have, assuming that most clinicians, and especially play therapists, would be well versed in this. Instead, my focus is to share the value and methods of involving kids and canines in play therapy in humane and clinically appropriate ways, and how this approach has the potential to facilitate practitioners' work and progress with children.

ANIMAL EMOTIONS AND
THE HUMAN-ANIMAL BOND

What I learned is that dogs have feelings, too. I never even thought of that when I used to hurt them before. I think I was just passing along all the bad things that happened to me. Now, dogs are really my friends – some of my BEST friends.
                              -Eddie, 16-year-old adopted boy with a
                              trauma history (from his journal)

Recent years have seen an explosion of scientific and popular books, articles, studies, websites, and television programs devoted to the human-animal bond. While animals have played a prominent role in science and literature for a long time, the wide range of topics, the focus on animal emotions and human-animal attachment, and the sheer volume of resources available today suggest a revitalized interest in all things animal. Materials come from many sources: biologists, veterinarians, ethologists, researchers, writers, social scientists, mental health practitioners, photographers, and ordinary people who want to share their experiences with animals. As scientific inquiry has increased the knowledge about the functions, mechanisms, and manifestations of emotions and social bonding in nonhuman animals, it has also contributed to the understanding of human emotions and attachment. Furthermore, much more is being learned about the role of interspecies relationships, especially human-animal bonds, and their positive and negative implications for those involved in them.

ANIMAL EMOTIONS

Many animals in addition to humans show emotions that are similar, perhaps identical, to those we call fear, joy, happiness, embarrassment, resentment, jealousy, rage, anger, love, pleasure, compassion, respect, relief, disgust, sadness, despair, and grief. Indeed, it is the shared emotions, their expression, and similar physiological and anatomical bases that truly blur the borders between them and us.
                              -Jane Goodall (*The Ten Trusts*)

It is no longer fruitful to ask if animals experience emotions, but, rather, why emotions have evolved – what functions they serve. The study of animal emotions, like the study of other behavior patterns,

depends on a careful blending of anecdotes, common sense, and "hard" empirical data. None of these are dispensable, despite skeptics' denial of the importance of good animal tales.
-Marc Bekoff (*The Ten Trusts*)

For a long time, the mere mention of animal emotions or internal states drew the criticism of anthropomorphism (ascribing human emotions to animals) within scientific circles. While people sometimes do inaccurately project complex human motivations, intentions, and characteristics onto animal behaviors, the scientific climate seems to have opened sufficiently to permit modern theorizing, investigation, and discussion of animals' emotions and their links to behavior and relationships. Many people are not aware that Darwin (1872/1965) explored comparative emotional expression in humans and animals. Careful analyses of case studies and qualitative research have demonstrated the breadth and depth of animal emotions (e.g., Masson, 1997; Masson & McCarthy, 1995; Thomas, 1993), but they have often been dismissed because of their lack of empirical "rigor." More recently, the fields of neurobiology and psychobiology have enhanced the understanding of animal emotions in fundamental ways (e.g., Panksepp, 2005a, 2005b; Siviy, 1998; Siviy, Harrison, & McGregor, 2006). A wonderful DVD, *Why Dogs Smile and Chimpanzees Cry* (Fleisherfilm, 1999), uses fascinating film footage and interviews with biologists, animal behaviorists, and wildlife filmmakers to show convincingly that emotions and relationships play a critical role in animal survival and well-being.

There seems little question today that animals and people share many of the same physiological and behavioral responses that are indicative of emotions, and they often seek similar social attachments and relationships that help many species survive and thrive. Animal behaviors are no longer considered solely to be mechanistic expressions of instinctual drives; rather, they represent a combination of genetic, biological, and environmental processes, much like human behavior. Animals are capable of a wide range of emotions, complex thinking, decision making, compassion, problem solving, and even fair play (Bekoff, 2004, 2007; Goodall & Bekoff, 2002; Panksepp, 2005a). Greater understanding of the origins and expression of animal emotions has the potential to improve human-animal relationships to the benefit of both.

THE HUMAN-ANIMAL BOND

If you talk to the animals, they will talk to you and you will know each other. If you do not talk to them, you will not know them. And what you do not know, you will fear. What one fears, one destroys.
-Chief Dan George

The origins of human bonds with animals are shrouded in the mists of the distant past. Of course, past generations and indigenous peoples have lived in closer contact with the natural world than most people do today. Some animals have shared special bonds with humans for thousands of years, perhaps because these liaisons were mutually beneficial to survival. Animals worked with humans in exchange for shelter, food, or protection from predators and the elements. For example, archaeological evidence suggests that wolves lived in close contact with humans as long as 300,000 years ago and that dogs were the first domesticated animal, involved intimately with humans for at least 14,000 years (Clutton-Brock, 1995). For centuries, animals have assisted people with the tasks of living, such as horses transporting people and goods, and dogs hunting and herding in conjunction with human hunters and shepherds. These early functional relationships provided the foundations for current-day bonds that are now derived more from companionship and mutually enjoyable ventures than from working relationships (Katz, 2003).

The history of animal-human bonds and their benefits to both people and animals are reviewed in a variety of resources (Beck & Katcher, 1996, 2003; Becker & Morton, 2002; Douglas, 2006; Jalongo, 2004; Knapp, 1998; Melson, 2001; Podberscek, Paul, & Serpell, 2000; Schoen, 2001; Serpell, 1995, 1996). Hart (1995) has reviewed studies demonstrating that dogs provide companionship, mutual support, a sense of belonging, security, and social lubricant effects. There is substantial evidence that most families consider their pets to be full-fledged family members with whom they sometimes feel closer than with their human relatives (Bonas, McNicholas, & Collis, 2000).

Studies have found positive human physiological reactions to animals, including lowered blood pressure and heart rates, improved cardiovascular health, better recovery after serious illness or surgery, and reduced stress reactions coupled with greater relaxation (Becker & Morton, 2002; Fine, 2000, 2006; Friedmann, Thomas, & Eddy, 2000).

S. B. Barker and R. T. Barker (1988) describe a 1984 *Psychology Today* survey of 13,000 pet owners who believed that pets improved the quality of family relationships by reducing tensions and increasing fun, compassion, conversation, exercise, time spent together, and affection shown for other family members.

CHILDREN'S RELATIONSHIP WITH ANIMALS

> *Companion animals should matter to educators, if for no other reason than that they matter so much to children.*
> -Mary Renck Jalongo

Animals play an important role in the lives of children (Jalongo, 2004; Melson, 2001). Children frequently draw animals, talk about animals, and even dream about animals. Many families obtain companion animals (pets) at the request of their children, and family dynamics, both healthy and dysfunctional, often incorporate the animals, as well (Hoover, 2006; Katz, 2003). When families relinquish pets against the wishes of children, it often has negative repercussions for the children for a very long time (Melson, 2001), including feelings of sadness, anger, worry, and loss.

Although child interactions with animals entail many responsibilities and drawbacks such as injuries to children and pets, allergies, and zoönoses (animal-related diseases), there are many advantages offered by the child-animal bond. Pets provide companionship to children, and many children consider them "friends." Guerney's (1991) study of latchkey children found that pets played an important role in children's coping with being home alone after school. Many other studies have found that children with companion animals have higher self-esteem, greater empathy, more engagement with peers, and other prosocial behaviors (Jalongo, 2004).

Children with a wide range of psychological and behavioral problems also seem to respond positively to animals. A common characteristic of children with abuse histories is that they are cruel to animals, yet when they are shown how to interact safely and kindly with animals and are supervised properly, their cruel behaviors are often replaced by empathy. Gonski (1985) found that the mere presence of a dog helped very distressed children in foster care quickly move from hostility, withdrawal, and resistance to much greater engagement, enthusiasm, laughter, and conversation.

Readers are urged to read the superb books by Melson (2001), Jalongo (2004), and Chandler (2005) for summaries of the research on child-animal bonds and thorough descriptions of the value of including animals in educational and therapeutic settings. Not only can children's negative behaviors toward animals be eliminated, but children's positive experiences with animals can help them educationally, developmentally, emotionally, and socially, and they can shape children's attachments – with animals and with people – throughout the child's life.

ANIMAL-ASSISTED THERAPY

When we first walked into the therapist's office and saw the two big Poodles, I wondered if I'd made a mistake. It was not at all what I expected. Later I realized how much those dogs – and the therapist, of course – helped our family.
    -Sylvie, mother of a 15-year-old boy

When I saw the Poodles, it changed my whole attitude. At first, I didn't want to go to counseling, but then I thought it couldn't be all bad if they had dogs there. Curly and Queenie helped me feel more comfortable there.
    -David, the 15-year-old boy

Animal-assisted therapy (AAT) has built upon the benefits of the human-animal bond in order to assist therapeutic progress in a variety of professions, including psychotherapy. The Delta Society (2004) has defined AAT as follows:

AAT is a goal-directed intervention in which an animal meeting specific criteria is an integral part of the treatment process. AAT is delivered and/or directed by a health/human service provider working within the scope of his/her profession. AAT is designed to promote improvement in human physical, social, emotional, and/or cognitive functioning. (p. 11)

In AAT, animals have been used for rapport-building; decreasing anxiety; developing trust; fostering attachment; increasing openness; adding emotional safety; improving motivation; and developing physical, cognitive, emotional, and social competencies. Animals have been used as a catalyst for social interactions and to decrease resistance. Animal involvement in therapeutic processes has ranged from the mere presence of animals in a therapeutic setting to full incorporation of animals in a wide range of therapeutic tasks. As the field of AAT has grown, efforts have been made to define it more clearly, establish standards for practice, and conduct research.

Animal-assisted therapy has been developing steadily since its early use by psychologist Boris Levinson (Levinson & Mallon, 1997) in psychological assessment, psychotherapy, residential treatment, education, and family therapy. Several excellent resources detail the practice of AAT, including its history, methods, training, applicability, ethical guidelines, and research (Chandler, 2005; Delta Society, 2004; Fine, 2000, 2006). Many different animals have been employed in AAT programs, including horses, dogs, cats, birds, rabbits, gerbils, reptiles, and dolphins.

Applications of AAT and the animal-human bond have been explored and researched by professionals from a variety of fields, such as biology, ethology, neuroscience, animal behaviorism, human and veterinary medicine, education, human development, and psychology. Because of this variety of theoretical and methodological orientations, it can be challenging to evaluate and draw conclusions about the body of work that has been done. In fact, it seems that the lack of multidisciplinary dialog has led some professionals in psychology, human development, and their related clinical fields to a common, but inaccurate conclusion that there is no support for the efficacy of AAT.

THE USEFULNESS OF AAT

Studies have shown AAT to be valuable for a variety of problem areas, such as children with autism (Sams, Fortney, & Willenbring, 2006), posttraumatic stress disorder (Altschuler, 1999), youth maladjustment and conflict with parents (Strand, 2004), chronic medical conditions (Gorczyca et al., 2006), adolescent anger management (Hanselman, 2001), and for effective differential diagnosis of several child problems (Prothmann et al., 2005). Animals have been used successfully in mental health programs (Carpenter, 2005; Fine, 2006; Hayden, 2005; Kruger & Serpell, 2006; Woolley, 2005), speech therapy (Adams, 1997), and educational and residential settings (e.g., Jalongo, 2004; Jalongo, Astorino, &

Bomboy, 2004; Sullivan, 2006; www.cbryouthconnect.org; www.greenchimneys.org; www.gressmountainranch.com).* AAT has also been used in youth correctional and detention facilities (e.g., Bondarenko, 2007; Loar & Colman, 2004) and for crisis response with child and family victims and rescue personnel at disaster sites (Greenbaum, 2006; Kohr, 2006; Shane, 2006).

The body of research evidence that demonstrates the value of AAT continues to grow. Chandler (2005) has reviewed studies that show a positive impact of AAT in a number of arenas: psycho-physiological health, anxiety, dementia, depression, motivation, self-esteem enhancement, children in pediatric hospitals, children with developmental disorders, children and adolescents with emotional and behavioral problems, elderly people, physically disabled people, and psychiatric patients. In two editions, Fine (2000, 2006) has thoroughly discussed research methodology and protocols, reliable and valid measures, and the current status of empirical support for AAT. A recent meta-analysis of AAT showed moderate effect sizes for improvements in several problem areas, and the use of dogs was associated with moderately high effect size (Nimer & Lundahl, 2007). Although enthusiasm for AAT is widespread and empirical studies have shown its potential value, more research on its processes, outcomes, and applications will strengthen its place in mental health treatment.

AAT CREDENTIALS

A number of certification programs have been developed, often in conjunction with training programs. A good first step toward therapy certification is the American Kennel Club's (AKC) Canine Good Citizen® certification (www.akc.org, then search "CGC"). The program was developed to encourage appropriate training for dogs so that they behave well at home and in the community. It is open to all dogs and owners. This program, developed in the United States in 1989, has been adopted for use in many other countries, as well. It provides a good indication whether a dog has had sufficient training to move into more advanced canine therapy training programs.

The best known animal-assisted therapy certification programs include those of the Delta Society (www.deltasociety.org; Delta Society,

---

*Although all websites cited in this monograph were correct at the time of publication, they are subject to change at any time.

2004) and Therapy Dogs International (TDI; www.tdi-dog.org). Potential therapy dogs and their handlers must meet specified criteria before being certified. Having one of these credentials and maintaining active membership also provides insurance that covers the use of therapy dogs in most settings.

PLAY AND PLAY THERAPY

> *How come dogs know how to play and grown-ups don't?*
> -Val, 5-year-old girl

Many animals, including humans, play actively during their formative years and to a lesser extent, throughout their lives. The ability to read play signals and to interact through play behaviors often crosses species lines (Bekoff, 2007). Play bows and play faces signal "no harm intended" in order to initiate and maintain play in much the same way that children's statement of "Let's pretend" communicates that all that follows is imaginative and "not for real." There are many similarities between the play of humans and that of other animals, perhaps explaining why cross-species play is possible.

ANIMAL PLAY

> *Play confers a freedom that is not available in any other realm of a dog's life. No wonder they enjoy it and want to engage in it so often.*
> -Jeffrey Moussaieff Masson
> (*Dogs Never Lie About Love*)

Studies of animal play provide a unique perspective on human play. A few key resources are highlighted here. Bekoff and Byers (1998) compiled the work of key animal play researchers to explore a wide range of play behaviors and their possible functions, including play as a means to facilitate learning, enhance cognitive development, increase response options, and improve the ability to "read" and react to complex environmental conditions. Pellegrini and P. K. Smith (2005) compare human play with that of the great apes, focusing on different types of play, such as object play, social play, and fantasy play. Burghardt (2005) has proposed useful criteria for defining play behaviors across species that distinguish play from exploratory or stereotypical behaviors that might be similar. Although for years play was considered to occur only in mammals and birds, current studies applying these criteria are exploring potential play behaviors in alligators, Komodo dragons, shrimp, lobsters, turtles, octopi, fish, and even ants and other insects!

An informative article about animal play in the December 1994 issue of *National Geographic* is accompanied by compelling photographs depicting the play lives of a wide range of animals (Brown, 1994). Brown, a psychiatrist, provides useful information through his National Institute for Play (www.nifplay.org). His video series, *The Promise of Play*, broadly covers human and animal play, positing new insights into play behavior (Brown & Kennard, 2000).

Psychobiological research has also contributed to our understanding of play. Panksepp's (2005a, 2005b) work on the neuroanatomical and neurochemical mechanisms of emotion in the mammalian brain includes studies of rough-and-tumble play and laughter in rats. The release of endogenous opioids during play seems to modulate play behaviors. Siviy (1998) has elucidated the role of dopamine in energizing animals just prior to play, and the influence of norepinephrine and serotonin in modulating play once it has begun. McConnell (2005, 2006) has convincingly summarized the similarities of canine and human expressions that correlate with the mechanisms revealed by neurobiological studies, and she has suggested that the high affective expressiveness of both species may account for their proclivity to interact, play, and bond with each other.

Finally, recent studies and articles have explored the evolution of social behavior and morality in animals, looking at cooperation, compassion, forgiveness, negotiation, and fair play and their implications for human behavior and humans' interactions with animals (Allen & Bekoff, 2005; Bekoff, 2004, 2007). The four examples below represent commonly seen "social handicapping" that keeps social play alive for the animals or children involved:

> Kirrie now has a new play partner, a third Beagle we added to the household when an ill relative could no longer care for him. Kirrie and Pugsy engage in rough housing and play fighting for long periods. Kirrie is considerably larger, stronger, and more agile than Pugsy. Kirrie could easily win every tug-of-war game they play with rope toys. Nevertheless, Kirrie appears to drop the toy deliberately (she has it firmly in her mouth and then widens her jaws to let it fall out) so that Pugsy can "win" about one third of their bouts. If she

did not permit Pugsy some success, he would likely lose interest and stop playing, so to keep the game going, she "takes turns" winning.

A similar process happens when children play during nondirective play sessions with a therapist or during filial play sessions with one of their parents. For example, when playing "store" with her mother, 5-year-old Jesse charged huge sums of money ("gazillions of dollars") for various items that her mother would pretend to purchase. Jesse happily took all of the play money that her mother had. When she saw that her mother had no money left, she added, "and here's your change" and gave her mother a new handful of dollars. She repeated this sequence over and over. She clearly wanted to enact a purchasing exchange, and when she saw that the game would be over unless her mother had more money, she gave her more dollars to keep the interaction going.

During any unsupervised sandlot baseball or softball game among children, there are arguments about the rules. "He's out!" "No, he's safe." "Nunh unh, He's out by a mile!" I know because I spent many adolescent summers with the neighborhood gang, playing ball and arguing. The arguments, vehement as they were, somehow always got settled. If we didn't mutually agree to go on, or if we had resorted to violence, the game would have ended. We let go of strongly held beliefs about specific situations for the sake of the game. Although we didn't know it at the time, we were most likely developing some social negotiation skills, much as dogs and other animals do!

Thirteen-year-old Bryce frequently had "melt-downs" whenever he began to lose during games with his friends or family. He could not tolerate feeling like a failure. Even so, when he played a tug game with a play therapy dog, he readily let go of the rope toy and "lost" in order to continue the interaction. His desire to play with the dog seemed to override his fear of losing.

The references on animal play cited in this section are fascinating and thought provoking. They provide a multidisciplinary understanding of the possibilities that cross-species play seems to offer in the therapy context.

HUMAN PLAY

We are playful mammals all our lives and that has been the reason for our remarkable adaptability and achievement as a species.
                                                                    -Ashley Montagu

Research has shown that children who play often – both solitarily and socially – become more creative and imaginative than those whose exposure to play and toys is limited.
-Brian Sutton-Smith

Play is universal among children, and it seems to guide important developmental processes. It promotes healthy connections in the brain and strengthens intellectual, physical, emotional, social, and creative processes. It releases stress and stimulates problem solving. It is an integral feature of parent-child attachment, which in turn is vital for healthy developmental and psychosocial functioning. These points seem to have general consensus among developmental and clinical professionals. Less is known, however, about the mechanisms through which play works in the child's life, and some common assertions about the value of play have yet to be researched thoroughly.

Present-day trends that highly structure children's play may be detracting from the evolutionary, social, developmental or other purposes served by children's natural spontaneous play (Elkind, 2007a, 2007b). Children's play has increasingly become more solitary, restricted, and structured, to such an extent that the American Academy of Pediatrics has issued a report warning of possible negative implications (Ginsburg, 2007). It seems that the natural free play of children is facing extinction, with many professionals, including therapists, worried about deleterious effects on children's psychosocial well-being.

PLAY THERAPY

We can be sure that all happenings, pleasant or unpleasant, in the child's life, will have repercussions on her dolls.
-Jean Piaget

In order to use canines in play therapy, one must have thorough knowledge, training, and experience in play therapy. VanFleet (2004) has described play therapy as

a broad field that uses children's natural inclination to play as a means of creating an emotionally safe therapeutic environment that encourages communication, relationship-building, expression, and problem resolution for the child. (p. 5)

Wilson and Ryan (2005) have defined the role of play therapy in fostering healthy child development as:

> relationship experiences between therapists and children or young people, in which play is the principal medium of communication. In common with adult therapies, the aim of these experiences is to bring about changes in an individual's primary relationships, which have been distorted or impaired during development. The aim is to bring children to a level of emotional and social functioning on par with their developmental stage, so that usual developmental progress is resumed. (pp. 3-4)

Play therapists initially study child development, family development, personality theories, psychopathology, and psychotherapy in their preparation for clinical practice, usually earning a master's or doctoral degree in a mental health field. They must know what to expect and how to respond to children's play behaviors during therapy sessions and how to accurately interpret the possible meanings of children's play themes within the contexts of the child's life. They recognize signs of progress as manifested in children's play sessions, such as trauma mastery play, and in daily life, such as reduced behavior problems or improved emotional regulation. They have the ability to apply or design play-based interventions that help children meet therapeutic goals.

Play therapy approaches are as diverse as the theoretical orientations behind them, ranging from psychodynamic and humanistic through cognitive-behavioral (e.g., Gil, 1991; Kaduson, Cangelosi, & Schaefer, 1997; Kaduson & Schaefer, 2000, 2006; Kottman, 1995; Landreth, 2002; O'Connor & Schaefer, 1994; Schaefer & O'Connor, 1983; Terr, 1990; VanFleet, 2006a; Webb, 1999; Wilson & Ryan, 2005). Play therapy is often divided into two major categories, directive and nondirective, within which the many forms fall. Nondirective play therapies typically provide the child with a wide range of toys or play items in a therapeutic climate emphasizing emotional safety and acceptance. The child selects the items with which to play and the activities, while the therapist maintains acceptance through empathic listening and child-centered imaginary play, and safety through structuring and limit-setting. The therapist follows the child's lead, assuming that in this climate, children will move in the direction of greater health. In directive play therapies, the therapist typically selects the materials and/or the activities to address more directly the specific treatment goals for the child. In all forms of play therapy, the therapist remains attuned to the child's needs, allowing those needs to guide decisions about what actually happens during play sessions. All approaches to play therapy use a playful, relatively light-hearted approach with the child, as it is the playfulness that provides the emotional safety in which the child can then express and work through issues. Furthermore, play therapists recognize the importance of a strong therapeutic relationship with the child, as that provides the context in which the child's therapeutic work is possible. Parents are involved in the play therapy process through regular consultations or directly in the play sessions, as in Filial Therapy (VanFleet, 2005).

Because quality play therapy is so developmentally attuned, using children's natural play processes to help them learn and grow in healthy directions, it has a successful track-record with a wide range of child and family challenges, such as aggression, anxiety, attachment problems, depression, grief, abuse and neglect, traumatic events, autistic spectrum disorders, bipolar disorder, oppositional behaviors and conduct problems, perfectionism and obsessive-compulsive disorder, family substance abuse, domestic violence, medical illness, divorce, step-families, foster families, and adoption. Many resources on the web offer more information, such as the Association for Play Therapy (www.a4pt.org), the British Association of Play Therapists (www.bapt.info), the International Collaborative on Play Therapy (www.play-therapy.com, then click on *International*), and at the author's website (www.play-therapy.com).

RESEARCH ON PLAY THERAPY

The quantity and quality of empirical research on play therapy is growing rapidly. A meta-analysis of 94 controlled play therapy studies showed that play therapy and Filial Therapy are effective ways to treat child problems in a relatively short-term manner (Bratton et al., 2005). In a book published by the American Psychological Association, Reddy, Files-Hall, and Schaefer (2005) have compiled descriptions of play therapy approaches with strong empirical bases used for a wide range of difficulties. VanFleet, Ryan, and S. K. Smith (2005) have reviewed over 40 years of research on Filial Therapy, which has consistently demonstrated its ability to bring about positive changes for children and their families. Play therapy has gained greater recognition in recent years due to the quantity and quality of the evidence.

PLAY THERAPY CREDENTIALS

In the United States, play therapists typically are licensed in their primary mental health field, such as psychiatrist, psychologist, social worker, counselor, marriage and family therapist, school counselor, and so on. The Registered Play Therapist and the Registered Play Therapist-Supervisor credentials are earned as secondary credentials through the Association for Play Therapy (www.a4pt.org) and show that the professional has met substantial training and supervised practice requirements. Other play therapy organizations offer their own credentials in the United States and in some other countries. In the United Kingdom and Ireland, play therapy has emerged as its own profession, and national governmental standards for its practice are under consideration. The British Association of Play Therapists (www.bapt.info) has established a credentialing process, and several universities have post-master's play therapy training programs. Play therapy is emerging as a viable field in many other countries, and professional organizations to ensure quality training and practice are arising, as well. The International Collaborative on Play Therapy (www.play-therapy.com, then click on *International*) has been developed to facilitate information sharing and dialog about play therapy worldwide.

It is critical that the canine-assisted interventions described in this book be implemented either directly by, or under the supervision of, a properly trained and credentialed play therapist or supervisor.

INTEGRATION OF ANIMAL-ASSISTED THERAPY AND PLAY THERAPY

Animals are such agreeable friends – they ask no questions, they pass no criticisms.
                                                            -George Eliot

The fields of animal-assisted therapy (AAT) and play therapy (PT) developed independently of each other, and in recent years, both approaches have gained greater recognition and acceptance among mental health, medical, educational, and other professionals. The bodies of research in each of these fields have grown substantially, and empirical support has provided a foundation for wider dissemination. AAT and PT also share some common assumptions and goals about healing and enriching children's lives. It seems that an integration of the two approaches has the potential to enhance practitioners' clinical work with children and families in novel and substantial ways.

AAT and PT are both broad fields, with a wide range of theoretical orientations, goals, specific methods, and applications contained within each. There have been animal-assisted therapists who have used play-based interventions in their work, and there have been play therapists who have incorporated their pets and other animals into the play therapy process. Even so, there is very little written about the combined use of principles and methods from both AAT and PT in clinical practice. Moreover, there seem to be few practitioners from each of these fields who are trained and/or credentialed in the other. A description of this integrated approach is included here.

ANIMAL-ASSISTED PLAY THERAPY/PET PLAY THERAPY

Clinical practice that integrates AAT with PT has developed into its own field quite recently and, as such, does not have a commonly used moniker. It has variously been called *animal-assisted play therapy*, *pet play therapy*, *canine-assisted play therapy*, and *play therapy with canine (or animal) cotherapists*. These terms are used interchangeably in this monograph to refer to the combined approach of AAT and PT.

VanFleet (2007a) has offered a definition of this emerging field:

> Animal-assisted play therapy is the use of animals in the context of play therapy, in which appropriately trained therapists and animals engage with children and families primarily through systematic play interventions, with the goal of improving children's developmental and psychosocial health as well as the animal's well-being. Play and playfulness are essential ingredients of the interactions and the relationship. (p. 17)

This definition highlights several key features: (a) the therapist and animal are trained to do this type of work; (b) the interventions are systematic in nature, with forethought and evaluation of their usefulness in terms of therapeutic goals; (c) the primary modality of the interventions is play, including cross-species play; (d) the interventions are beneficial to the child developmentally and/or clinically; (e) the animal employed should benefit from the work, as well; and (f) there is a focus on the various relationships of all those involved with each other – child, therapist, and animal.

Many of these features are considered cornerstones of ethical, effective play therapy as well as child therapy in general. Adding the services of a trained therapy animal need not, and should not, alter the focus on the child's progress and well-being. Considering the animal's well-being as well as the child's is vital for several reasons: First, if the animal does not enjoy or benefit from the work, then it is likely to become stressed and lose motivation. That process erodes its effectiveness as a cotherapist. Second, in such situations, the therapist serves as an important role model for the child, especially in terms of how to care for and interact with animals. When the therapist shows concern for the therapy animal's well-being, children are watching and learning. Third, children may draw conclusions about their own care from the manner in which the therapist treats the animal. At all times, it is vital for the therapist to demonstrate genuine concern, not only for the child but for the animal, as well.

It should be noted that there are different ways to structure animal-assisted play therapy, and these are covered in the section on practical management. Play therapists sometimes use their own pets as cotherapists, preferably after they have been properly socialized and trained for this work. An alternative is for play therapists to invite animal-assisted therapists or other trained handlers to join them in providing services to children and families. When two professionals are involved in jointly providing interventions, it is important that they each understand the other's field and general nature of interventions. Dialog and multidisciplinary education are essential.

EXPLORATORY STUDIES OF ANIMALS IN PLAY THERAPY

Although some case study information is available about the use of animals in play therapy, research is needed on this emerging practice.

Thompson (2007) is currently conducting the first known controlled study of dogs integrated into play therapy. Several other qualitative and quantitative studies are planned. One purpose in writing this monograph has been to increase awareness of the potential use of canines in play therapy so that a greater pool of play therapists using dogs can be included in more rigorous future research.

VanFleet (2007b) has completed an exploratory, qualitative study of the use of animals by play therapists in their work with children and families. Because virtually nothing was known about the use of animals in play therapy settings, a survey with open-ended questions was used to determine the ways that play therapists have been using animals. It was hoped that the survey would yield information valuable to guide further hypotheses and research questions. The study is ongoing, but a brief report based on 83 respondents is currently available.

Play therapists reported the use of a wide range of animals, with dogs being the most common. Fewer than half of the respondents had substantial training in animal-assisted therapy, but most had trained their animals for obedience. Survey respondents were enthusiastic about the value of animals in play therapy, citing advantages such as anxiety reduction, empathy development, positive tactile experiences, confidence-building, self-regulation, and healthy attachment experiences. Overwhelmingly, the play therapists reported that children were exceptionally responsive to the involvement of animals in play therapy. The current report is available in its entirety at www.play-therapy.com, under *Pets in PT* or at www.playfulpooch.org.

A FOCUS ON CANINES

The remainder of this monograph focuses on the use of canines in play therapy, because a full exploration of a wide range of animals would exceed space limitations. Dogs are uniquely suited for play therapy work, and they are perhaps most readily available to the greatest number of play therapists. Nevertheless, many different animals have a great deal to offer children and families, and the healing power of cats, horses, rabbits, and other animals is not to be underestimated.

"THE ORIGINAL
PLAY THERAPISTS":
A CASE FOR CANINES

*Man is troubled by what might be called the Dog Wish, a strange
and involved compulsion to be as happy and carefree as a dog.*
-James Thurber *(And So to Medve)*

A full exploration of the range of animals with potential value in
play therapy would take much more space than is intended for this
monograph. The remainder of the monograph, therefore, focuses on
the species of nonhuman animal that seems to be most readily suited to
play therapy work – canines. While cats, rabbits, lizards, birds, and
many other animals have unique and substantial benefits to offer the
practice of play therapy, they are not within the scope of this volume.
Melson (2001) provides a wonderful exploration of the importance of
animals in children's development, and Jalongo (2004) offers an excellent
description of the use of a wide range of animals in educational and
international settings with children. Much of their work has implications
for child therapy and play therapy as well.

It is hoped that the descriptions of canines in play therapy provided
here will prompt thought, discussion, innovation, and research not only
with dogs, but with a wide range of species that might be suitable for
this type of work. Many of the considerations and ideas outlined here
may provide an impetus for thoughtful development of this field in
broader ways.

WHY DOGS? A CASE FOR CANINES

*I could never take dogs for granted. . . . They were just animals, after
all, and it seemed to me that their main preoccupation ought to be in
seeking food and protection; instead they dispensed a flow of
affection and loyalty which appeared to be limitless.*
-James Herriot *(James Herriot's Dog Stories)*

Some of the unique characteristics of the human-canine bond have
been described elsewhere (Hart, 1995; Katz, 2005; Serpell, 1995). Dogs
have compelling features that make them uniquely suited to involvement
in play therapy. VanFleet (2007a) has described them as "the original

play therapists" because of this. Some of the factors that highlight dogs' suitability specifically for play therapy work follow.

First, many children of all ages from various cultures are drawn to dogs and enjoy interacting with them. When children see a dog at a park or public place, they often look, point, reach out, or try to communicate with the dog. An example follows.

> Recently my Border Collie mix, Kirrie, accompanied me to a busy hotel near New York City where we copresented a pet play therapy workshop. In addition to workshop attendees, the hotel served many international families and travelers. As I walked in the lobby with Kirrie, two small girls were waiting alongside their mother who was using the public telephone. They saw Kirrie, immediately smiled and pointed, and made exclamations in a language I did not recognize. I smiled at the children but did not approach them as I did not want to frighten them or their mother, especially when her attentions were on her phone conversation. The children continued to call to the dog, and I gave them a friendly wave and kept walking. Then their language shifted to one I understood clearly – that universal canine language of howling. The girls filled the lobby with high-pitched "ah-roo, ah-roo" sounds, laughing with delight and then waving at Kirrie and me.

Play has often been called the universal language of children, but this example illustrates both the "draw" dogs seem to have for many children as well as another universal language – that of "dog." Jalongo (2004) has stated the importance of involving animals that so readily captivate children: "Companion animals should matter to educators, if for no other reason than that they matter so much to children" (p. 17). The same seems true of mental health and play therapy professionals who work to help children developmentally and clinically.

Second, most dogs are quite playful and remain so throughout their lives. There are individual differences in playfulness, but it does appear to be a prevalent trait. Dogs play readily with other dogs, and they often engage easily in cross-species play, especially with children. When children and dogs meet, they often connect immediately on the play dimension. For many canines, this playfulness can be readily tapped for work within play therapy. Children and dogs both use play faces and postures to communicate their desire to play, and therapists can help them understand each other's communications and how to play safely with each other. This eagerness to play is one of the key "canine credentials" that suit them so well to play therapy.

When 8-year-old Bobby came for play therapy, he rarely smiled. He had been referred for school-related anxiety and withdrawn behaviors around his peers. He was a target for bullying and typically bore a serious, timid demeanor. After he learned how to play ball with Kirrie, she would often pick up the ball and drop it at his feet or nudge his arm to ask him to throw the ball for her. It was at these moments that Bobby laughed aloud and quickly joined in the game with the dog. He seemed enormously pleased that Kirrie wanted to play with him, a sense of belonging he sadly lacked from his human peers. His confidence grew, and he was able to relax and enjoy the play, and the other aspects of his play therapy progressed more rapidly thereafter. His teacher reported that he began speaking in class, relating stories of his interactions with Kirrie, and his classmates were responsive to that. His focus shifted away from himself, and he began to make friends more easily.

Third, dogs seem accepting and nonjudgmental in their relationships with people. They seem to show affection and a desire to interact without regard to children's physical appearance, mood, good or bad behavior, and so on. Children sense that dogs like them just for themselves, and this has a potential freeing effect in the therapeutic setting. Play therapists show acceptance of the child in many different types of play therapy, and dogs are in a position to facilitate a nonjudgmental climate in play sessions. This enhances the emotional safety of the play session environment, which in turn helps children use the play sessions to do their therapeutic work. No matter what happens from one session to the next, dogs seem happy to see the child each time and children feel as though they have a true friend with them.

Marianne, a self-conscious 12-year-old, told me that "Kirrie just likes me. She's like my grandma – they both like me no matter what I say or what I do. I wish everyone could be like that!"

Fourth, dogs seem to show empathy. They read people's signals and seem to sense different human moods and reactions. With children, many canines seem to adjust their own behavior to match the child's moods – becoming quieter when the child feels sad, standing back when the child is angry, and inviting the child to play when the child seems ready for it. Whether one believes these behaviors are genuine canine empathy or some other motivation at work, the key factor is that most people, including children, *believe* that it is genuine empathy. It *feels* genuine, and that seems sufficient to have strong therapeutic benefit.

> Many years ago, one of my 18-year-old clients, Karen, asked that I permit my Keeshond dog, Meisje, to sit in the room with us. Meisje would always sit or lie at her feet. When Karen spoke of difficult material or began to cry, Meisje always sat up, placed her head on the young woman's knee, and looked up into her eyes. Meisje also gently licked her arm or face when Karen bent over to stroke the dog. Karen always continued to discuss her concerns while this was happening, but she told me that Meisje "gives me the strength to go on. I feel like she's protecting me."

Fifth, dogs enjoy physical contact. Whether they are playing or resting, dogs often seek physical contact with the people in their lives, and this seems particularly true of children. Touch seems to be an important element of healing for children, and dogs can offer a safe medium of touch during play therapy. This physical contact can also be used to help abused children learn first-hand about safe and healthy touch. It can also serve as a calming force for both the child and the dog.

> Jagen, one of our Beagles, loves physical contact. She and her littermate, Corky, often create intricate "puppy piles" when sleeping, with their legs, heads, necks, and tails intertwined in various configurations. Jagen is especially fond of cuddling up next to people, no matter how hot the weather. She often slides her body along a person's leg or arm and goes to sleep. After a play session, 4-year-old Brian asked to pet Jagen. His mother and I agreed. Brian sat cross-legged on the floor. Jagen, who had recently eaten and was sleepy, slid along his thigh and promptly fell asleep. Brian sat quietly petting the length of Jagen's body and smoothing her ultra-soft ears while his mother and I scheduled the next session. His mother commented that she had never seen Brian so quiet unless he was asleep. His inability to calm himself down had been one of the presenting problems, yet he'd found a way to do it through his contact with Jagen.

Sixth, dogs often exhibit some of the same behavior or social problems that children do, such as hyperactivity, misbehavior, anxiety, or shyness. This fact can be used to prompt children to "help" the dog, thereby helping themselves. Rescued dogs have sometimes been victims of trauma as children have, and children can relate to dogs quite quickly when they share similar histories.

When 13-year-old Jordan learned that Kirrie had been in a shelter and then in a Border Collie rescue, much as he had experienced several foster homes, he immediately became interested in all the details about her. Throughout his play therapy interactions with her, he commented how she and he had similar problems, such as oppositional behaviors ("We're both stubborn"), trauma reactions ("She doesn't want anyone messing with her anymore"), and attachment concerns ("She's really lucky to get adopted").

Seventh, dogs are quite trainable and very adaptable. They are eager to please and learn quickly with repetition and the proper reinforcements. This gives them flexibility in the tasks that they can perform in play therapy. They enjoy learning new games and children can be involved in teaching them, thereby increasing their own competence and self-efficacy. Dogs often adjust readily to new children and situations.

A preschool child helped me train Meisje to shake hands and was thrilled that she could have that type of influence. She immediately wanted to show her parents her accomplishment and proudly demonstrated the "Shake" cue and praise ("Good Meisje!") after the dog shook hands with her.

Eighth, canines can be quite active. There is great variation among dogs on this characteristic, but active dogs can be used for some energetic play therapy activities that have potential benefits for motor development, weight loss, and physical competencies.

By the time Julia was 7 years old, she was significantly overweight. She resisted the exercises that her mother and father encouraged her to do, but she eagerly took a therapy dog for walks and played mildly active games with it. She focused much more on the dog's excitement during their mutual activities than on the discomfort of movement.

Ninth, canines are oriented to the here and now. They live in the present moment, which is consistent with play. This can be helpful for children who worry a great deal about the past or the future and whose anxieties prevent them from playing fully. As children engage in compelling play with the dog, they begin to experience some relief from their anxieties as their focus shifts to the present fun.

> Playing with Kirrie helped 11-year-old Clarissa set aside her obsessive worries about a difficult moment that had happened in school the day before. The dog continuously engaged her in a manner that did not give her any free time to worry. She experienced it as a big relief to get the trouble off her mind.

Tenth, dogs are social animals with a focus on attachment. They have aligned themselves in close relationship with humans for 14,000 years. Much of their behavior and reactions with people are geared toward creating harmonious relationships. Their ability to engage and connect with children can be a huge asset in involving children in the play therapy process, and they can enhance the trust that children feel toward the therapist and other people in their lives. The social lubricant effect of canines is pronounced, and it applies to therapeutic as well as social relationships.

> Cam had experienced abuse and neglect for much of his 9 years. A series of failed foster and adoptive placements had left him suspicious of all adults and most children. He had been slow to warm up to me, but when he had an opportunity to work and play with Kirrie, he seemed to relax much more in my presence, regardless of whether the dog was there. It appeared that he believed that an adult who would share her dog with him could not be all bad and perhaps unlike the adults who had harmed him.

These 10 characteristics of canines underscore their particular value to the play therapy process. Before therapists use a dog in play therapy, however, there are several important planning and preparatory tasks that must be considered. These include decisions about how the dog will be incorporated into their work, the selection and evaluation of a dog's suitability, and appropriate socialization and training of the dog and the therapist in handling the dog to ensure safety and beneficial outcomes for all involved. These are addressed in the two sections that follow.

CONSIDERATIONS FOR QUALITY, ETHICAL CANINE PLAY THERAPY PROGRAMS

If you treat dogs real nice, they love you more than anything!
-Reggie, 9-year-old foster child

Play therapy programs that systematically incorporate canines into the process need to be developed in a manner that serves the best interests of the client child and family as well as the animals that are involved. Standards and guiding principles for effective animal-assisted therapy programs have been described in detail elsewhere (Chandler, 2005; Fine, 2006), and Goodall and Bekoff (2002) have proposed 10 "trusts" that should guide our relationships and interactions with animals in general. Readers of the current monograph are urged to become familiar with these important resources on the sensitive, respectful, and humane treatment of animals. Clinicians are also bound by the ethical standards set for their practice with human clients, such as the American Psychological Association's *Ethical Principles of Psychologists and Code of Conduct* (2002).

The considerations that follow highlight some of the assumptions underlying the use of canines in play therapy. Different therapists may have different goals for different children at different times, so all of the considerations may not be operative all of the time. Nevertheless, they serve as guides to ensure that the program provides ethical and high quality treatment for all involved.

DEVELOPMENTAL SENSITIVITY

Canine play therapy programs facilitate or support the healthy development of children on several dimensions as needed, including physical, social, emotional, cognitive, behavioral, language, learning, and others. Developmentally realistic expectations are always considered when asking children or canines to engage in a particular activity. Play therapy and canine interventions are applied at a level that is developmentally appropriate for the child.

CLINICAL GROUNDING

Canine play therapy programs facilitate, support, or strengthen the children's and/or families' progress toward previously set therapeutic goals. Therapeutic goals should be established in a collaborative process with families and should take each child's unique personality and circumstances into account. The canine play therapy program is then used to further achievement of these goals, which may be social, emotional, behavioral, developmental, communicative, medical, or physical in nature. Good clinical practice comes first, and the incorporation of the dog into that comes second.

QUALITY OF LIFE

Canine play therapy programs enrich the children's and the dogs' lives by adding new experiences and opportunities for learning. The methods used are mutually beneficial to the children and the dogs.

COMPETENCE

Canine play therapy programs help children develop competencies, skills, and adaptive behaviors that contribute to present and future problem resolution and resilience. As children train and play with the dogs, both they and the dogs are learning things that foster good adjustment.

RELATIONSHIP ORIENTATION

Canine play therapy programs foster healthy attachment relationships between children and dogs that have the potential for facilitating and enhancing human relationships and attachments. Furthermore, the relationships developed between children and canines provide good models for children's future relationships with dogs.

NATURAL PROCESSES

Canine play therapy programs are centered on the natural developmental processes of both children and animals and the types of interactions that come naturally to each. Naturally occurring processes such as curiosity, empathy, attachment, play, and reciprocity provide the foundation for the canines' incorporation into the play therapy process. Expectations of the children and canines involved are kept within realistic boundaries; that is, neither is expected to learn difficult or unusual behaviors in order to relate to the other. Furthermore, play activities that are inspired or arise naturally from the dog's unique personality are preferred, as are play activities that are interesting and useful for the child.

PLAYFULNESS

Canine play therapy programs are playful and enjoyable for the children and the dogs involved. The interactions are characterized by smiles, laughter, licks, relaxed wagging tails, and other signs of mutual enjoyment. Not all of the interactions employed need be playful, but the focus is on interspecies play that benefits *both* of the players.

SAFETY

Canine play therapy programs assure the safety of children and dogs. *Physical safety* is promoted by proper preliminary training of the therapist and the play therapy dog as well as appropriate preparation of children as to how to approach and interact safely with canines. The therapist monitors the interactions for *emotional safety* of children and canines, as well. The therapist guards against undue stress for the children and the dogs by careful observation and vigilance during and after play sessions. The therapist also structures the time and space allotted for children and dogs and provides ways for play partners to calm down, relax, or stop the action completely.

GENERALIZATION OF LEARNING

Canine play therapy programs provide skills and experiences that children and canines can use in the future. Children may develop awareness and skills that they can apply in their own lives as well as with animals, pets, and people in the future. Dogs learn new skills, games, and flexible interactions that they can use in their future relationships, as well.

LIFE LESSONS

Canine play therapy programs capitalize on interactions or events that occur in the children's or the dogs' lives that can be used therapeutically to "teach" about life, emotions, relationships, and so on. The therapist helps the child understand lessons such as caring for another, staying safe, knowing one's limits, handling fears and frustrations, and calming oneself and others through the experiences that happen during the canine play therapy sessions or in the daily life of both child and dog.

SELECTING AND TRAINING
A PLAY THERAPY DOG

> *I own two dogs, and they both have been trained to respond immediately to my voice. For example, when we're outside, all I have to do is issue the following standard dog command: "Here Earnest! Here Zippy! C'mon! Here! I said come HERE! You dogs COME HERE RIGHT NOW! ARE YOU DOGS LISTENING TO ME? HEY!!!" And instantly both dogs, in unison, like a precision drill team, will continue trotting in random directions, sniffing the ground.*
> -Dave Barry *(Yellow Journalism)*

SELECTION OF PLAY THERAPY DOGS

Canine breeds not only have distinctive physical traits, but they also display a wide range of personalities. While there can be great variation within a particular breed that is influenced by the individual dog's biology, temperament, history of socialization, and other breeding (genetic) and environmental factors, different breeds do have general tendencies. Some are known for their ability to bond well with children while others may devote themselves to a single owner. Some are friendly, and others are aloof. There are many excellent sources of information about breed characteristics and temperaments (e.g., American Kennel Club, 1996, 2006; www.akc.org).

GENERAL CONSIDERATIONS

When selecting a dog for possible play therapy work, therapists should first consider their own personalities and preferences. They will spend a great deal of time with the dog, and it should be one that suits their own personality and needs. Factors such as energy level, need for exercise, tendency to bark and tolerance of noise, sociability, independence, ability to learn, size and space requirements, and adaptability, as well as a variety of owner characteristics and lifestyle factors, need to be considered. Katz (2005) and Pelar (2005) both provide thorough and practical guides for matching owners and dogs based on preferences, personalities, family lifestyle, and the unique individual characteristics of the dog.

Second, breed characteristics that have implications for work with children need to be considered, and there are many resources that describe these, including the American Kennel Club (AKC, 1996, 2006), but there is little or no research that clearly specifies certain breeds to be superior to others for work with children. Much depends on the nature of the work and the program goals for incorporating dogs into therapy. Many different breeds and mixes have been used successfully in therapy work, and the primary considerations must lie with the individual dog and how well it "fits" with the purposes and activities of the therapy program.

Third, the dog's own history should be considered. Acquiring a dog from a reputable breeder and inquiring about its early socialization experiences are exceptionally important. Chandler (2005) has detailed several tests that have potential for determining a dog's suitability for therapy work. Kalnajs (2006a, 2006b) has produced DVDs that clearly show how canine professionals use a dog's behavioral communication to evaluate its level of anxiety, stress, adaptability, and level of safety. She emphasizes that knowledge about canine communication is invaluable for families with dogs, for the safety and satisfaction of all. Her website, www.bluedogtraining.com, also has much useful information. Perhaps of greatest use for therapists wishing to use dogs in play therapy is Donaldson's (2005) *The Culture Clash*, which emphasizes the great importance of canine socialization and provides practical suggestions for the timing and type of socialization activities to use.

If a therapist is obtaining a potential therapy dog from a breeder, perhaps one of the best things therapist-owners can do is to participate in its socialization themselves. Gayle Kohr (personal communication, January 21, 2007), who has trained and used her own dogs as search and rescue, disaster relief, and therapy canines, was in the process of acquiring a puppy for potential therapy work at the same time this monograph was being written. She and her family visited the puppies at the breeder on a weekly basis from the time they were born. She was able to participate in their very early socialization, become familiar with the puppies' personalities, and eventually select the one that best suited her and her family and had the most promise for training as a therapy dog.

Mixed breed dogs can also make excellent play therapy dogs, but it is sometimes more difficult to determine their history of socialization and their prior experiences with people. Obtaining as much information as possible about the dog is important, and some dog trainers, shelters, rescue operations, and therapy dog organizations can provide useful information about a dog's suitability for therapy and service work (see Kalnajs, 2006a, 2006b). Beyond selection factors, appropriate socialization and training of all dogs are critical to prepare both the canine and its human handler, usually the therapist, for therapeutic work. Many personality and behavioral difficulties can be overcome through training although it is considerably more challenging with adult dogs (Donaldson, 2005).

The selection of a dog for therapy work is complex. Although a dog may be a wonderful pet, it may not necessarily be an appropriate canine therapist. Many factors must be weighed, including dog factors, therapist/handler factors, the relationship between the dog and therapist, the nature of the clients with whom the dog would work, the setting, and the goals for the canine's involvement. Guidelines have been developed to assist with the selection process (Fredrickson & Howie, 2000). Some of the most critical factors include reliability, predictability, controllability, suitability for the intended purposes, and the ability to inspire confidence.

ADDITIONAL CONSIDERATIONS
FOR CANINES IN PLAY THERAPY

Beyond the basic factors that generally make a good therapy dog, there are additional considerations when selecting a canine specifically for play therapy involvement. First, the dog needs to be playful, with sufficient energy to engage in play activities with children. Second, the dog should be friendly and comfortable with children of all ages and sizes. Third, the dog must be tolerant of confusion and the unpredictable movements, noises, and interactions that are typical of children in play therapy. Fourth, the dog should enjoy being touched, stroked, massaged, or groomed. Fifth, the dog should enjoy learning new "tricks" or activities. Sixth, the dog must not be possessive of toys or other items with which children play. (Resource guarding, as it is called by canine professionals, can be associated with aggressive behaviors that might be contraindicated for therapy work.) Finally, it is advantageous for the dog to be attentive to human affective expressions and to respond with the therapist's help and guidance to the child's needs.

Many of the case examples in this book feature my play therapy dog, Kirrie, who is a rescued Border Collie mix. She is very bright and learns exceptionally quickly. She has worked very well as a play therapy dog although her high energy level has implications for the types of interventions she can reasonably be expected to do (i.e., it would be unfair and unethical for me to expect her to lie around passively for hours at a time). She is one of the most energetic dogs I have ever had, and she requires a huge amount of exercise. As with many Border Collies, she needs to have a "job," or she creates one for herself, usually involving some sort of unintentional mischief. Although these active breeds – we also have three Beagles – fit well with our family lifestyle, they are not suited to everyone as pets or therapy dogs. Many Border Collies and Beagles are frustrating to owners who are unaware of their breed traits and who do not invest sufficient time socializing and training them, and these dogs frequently end up in shelters, ultimately being euthanized. While I would not automatically discount them from being play therapy dogs, I do not wish readers to think that they are necessarily the best breeds for this work either. Ultimately, after considering the suggestions in this section, it comes down to the individual dog and its "fit" with your personality, your lifestyle, the work that you have in mind for it, and your investment of time in its socialization and training. Even so, goals must be flexible, and as your relationship with the dog grows, your original plans might change while unanticipated possibilities may present themselves.

THE IMPORTANCE OF TRAINING

When a dog runs at you, whistle for him.
-Henry David Thoreau

Dogs with their canine ways do not automatically and instantly fit into the human world. They need to be trained and shown how to behave in ways that minimize the stress and disruption that often occurs when two species with very different "lifestyles" try to live together. A remarkable number of canine pets receive little or no training at all (Katz, 2005). Lack of training can result in negative outcomes, both for the dogs and for the families. In fact, animal behaviorists, dog trainers, canine rescue operators, veterinarians, and other canine professionals often attribute the high rates of canine euthanasia in the U.S. to behavior problems that most likely could have been prevented or resolved with basic training.

Most dog bites that are brought to medical attention in the U.S. each year are to children, and many of those are facial bites (McConnell, 2002, 2005; Melson, 2001; Pelar, 2005). Children often approach dogs with behaviors that put dogs on the defensive, and injury can result. McConnell (2002, 2005) has effectively argued that people often approach canines with primate behaviors, such as straight-on greetings and neck hugs, and these behaviors mean something very different to canines. Face-to-face greetings and hugs around the neck are often signals of aggression and ill-will in "canine-ese," and dogs respond by protecting themselves in one of the few ways that they can – with their mouths. Although training dogs in "bite inhibition" can prevent most of these reactions (Donaldson, 2005; Dunbar, 1996b), most dogs have not been taught to use their mouths safely with humans.

A better understanding of canine behaviors and signals can help owners provide smoother and safer integration of canines into family life. Many resources describe how to understand and/or communicate with dogs more accurately and fully (Becker & Spadafori, 2006; Masson, 1997; McConnell, 2002, 2005, 2006; Owens & Eckroate, 1999; Pelar, 2005), and Rugaas (2006) has described effective "calming signals" that are inherent in canine communications that can be used by owners to enhance their interactions with their dogs. The DVDs featuring Kalnajs (2006b) and McConnell (2006) are very useful, showing people how to understand a wide range of canine signals that are illustrated by video clips. Knowing how to read these canine communications helps people know when to approach, when to stay away, when to soothe, and when and what to communicate back to the dog to lead to the most successful outcomes. The best training seems to be a two-way street. People learn how to observe and understand the dog's language while gently showing the dog how to live in a human world. Compassion and reciprocity are important features of any good relationship!

In ways less serious than bites, dogs are responsible for other family distress, such as chewed furniture and books, broken toys, and "eaten" homework. It is easy to become frustrated with a dog when this happens, but often the problem stems from a lack of training and a lack of awareness of how human behavior influences canine behavior. Sometimes the dog is just being a dog, whereas its human family is expecting it to behave like a human. Tensions can arise from within the family system, too (Hoover, 2006). When the dog is not being blamed for human-canine problems, sometimes the children in a family are. Parents sometimes bring a dog into the family home after extracting from their children a promise "to take care of it." When the novelty of the new pet wears off, children easily can disregard their pet-care duties. Furthermore, parents sometimes expect that children are able to handle *all* of the pet responsibilities without supervision, and this seems an unreasonable expectation for most children, and especially for younger ones.

The stresses inherent in human-canine relationships when there is such misunderstanding of canine behavior or child development can result in neglected and anxious dogs, and in the worst case, in dogs that are mistreated, dropped along country roads, placed in shelters, and euthanized. Children in tense pet-related situations can develop fears of dogs, feelings of inadequacy, lack of motivation, and lifelong patterns of animal neglect or maltreatment.

Nearly all of these problems can be prevented or corrected with proper socialization and training, often requiring less than half an hour a day. As will be discussed later, one role that child and family therapists can play is to help families create more constructive, satisfying relationships with their pets. But first, therapists must train their own dogs who will eventually work with children in play therapy.

SOCIALIZATION AND BASIC TRAINING

It is quite wrong to attempt to instill obedience into a dog by punishment and equally senseless to beat him afterwards when, enticed by the scent of some game, he has run away during a walk. The beating will cure him not of running away, which lies farther back in his memory, but probably of the coming back, with which he will assuredly connect the punishment.
-Konrad Lorenz *(Man Meets Dog)*

Without thorough socialization and training, no dog should be used as a therapy dog. It is far too risky. Therapy dogs must be able to tolerate a wide range of interactions and situations, and they must respond reliably to verbal and nonverbal human cues to adjust their behavior, such as coming when called, sitting, lying down, staying, releasing items from their mouths, and refraining from barking.

Dog socialization and training methods have changed considerably through the years, and most dog trainers and animal behaviorists now prefer positive approaches. Socialization involves exposing dogs from puppyhood through adulthood to many different human and animal situations that help dogs become comfortable with a wide range of circumstances. Positive training involves the use of classical and operant conditioning principles to help dogs adapt their natural behaviors, with strong emphasis on the use of positive motivators for the dogs and complete avoidance of "choke and drag" methods and other aversives. Some socialization and training programs involve "play training" in which the dog learns various cues in the context of play. Many trainers suggest that the training focus is actually on the *human*, and when that is successful, the canine does well.

Amidst the vast number of books, videos, and television programs advocating various approaches to dog behavior and training, several stand out as exceptional resources on positive socialization and training (Donaldson, 2005; Dunbar, 1996a, 1996b; Overall, 1997). There are also excellent resources on raising children and canines together, as well as how to help children become involved in the training process (Dunbar, 1996a; Pelar, 2005; Silvani & Eckhardt, 2005; Weston & Ross, 2005). Information on the special training considerations for rescued/ adopted dogs are also available (Dennison, 2005; Donaldson, 2005). The positive methods outlined in these books make obsolete the use of punishment-oriented devices such as choke chains, prong collars, or shock collars. Furthermore, positive training is much more effective (as shown by the evidence), generalizes more readily, and strengthens the relationship between human and canine in a mutually respectful way. Many useful resources are available at www.dogwise.com.

The use of positive socialization and training approaches for dogs is particularly relevant to therapy work with children and families. Not only are there parallels with the positive parenting methods that therapists often encourage, but the use of nonaversive dog training methods helps therapists model safe, appropriate, and relationship-building approaches, demonstrating the respect and empathy that they wish to share with and instill in the children and families with whom they work.

Many dog owners take advantage of canine training programs offered by dog trainers and other canine professionals in their communities. This often is the best way to train a dog, and especially its owner. Organizations such as the Association of Pet Dog Trainers (www.apdt.com) help trainers keep abreast of current best practices, and they provide information and directories of local trainers that mental health professionals might engage for assistance in training their dogs. Trainers with the Certified Pet Dog Trainer (CPDT) credential are often most qualified to offer the positive training methods recommended for therapy dogs as well as pets. Mental health professionals can acquire the necessary socialization and training for themselves and their dogs by attending nonaversive canine training classes or doing it on their own, but they should bear in mind that abundant socialization and nonaversive training is critical for any dog and therapist planning to incorporate the canine in therapy.

When seeking a training program for themselves and their dogs, therapists should inquire about the training philosophy and approach that is used. Positive approaches are important not only for the dog, but also for the handler who is learning new skills! Training therapy dogs takes effort and patience with the dog and oneself, and it works best when both dog and handler are relaxed and enjoying themselves. Healthy relationships are at the core of child, parent, and family adjustment, and the same is true of the canine members of the family. When therapists hope to incorporate canines into play therapy, the use of preparatory approaches that combine (a) substantial socialization experiences; (b) positive behavioral methods; (c) knowledge of canine body language and signals; (d) continuous effort and patience; and (e) lots of excitement, fun, and play times seems to be the most likely to succeed and most congruent with the practice of play therapy.

THERAPY DOG TRAINING AND CERTIFICATION PROGRAMS

Several Animal-Assisted Therapy training and certification programs have been developed for dogs and their handlers. Practitioners who are considering the use of canine cotherapists are wise to work toward one of these nationally recognized certifications. They have been described in the section on AAT Credentials.

Chandler (2005) has provided some valuable tips for training a therapy dog, as well as a summary of the CGC, Delta Society, and TDI requirements. Other books on the use of therapy dogs in a variety of settings and situations also provide valuable information related to the training needed for this work (Fine, 2000, 2006; Levinson & Mallon, 1997; Loar & Colman, 2004).

PLAY THERAPY TRAINING
FOR CANINE AND THERAPIST

*People shouldn't yell at their dogs, because then the dogs are afraid
and hide. It's better if you give them treats and hug them and play
with them.*

-Jenny, 7-year-old girl

When a therapist uses a dog in play therapy, specialized training is
needed for both the therapist and the dog. For the therapist, a thorough
knowledge of the developmental, clinical, and family applications of
play therapy is absolutely essential. Without this background, case
decision making can be seriously compromised. Furthermore, a
credential entailing supervised practice, such as Registered Play
Therapist (in the United States) or Qualified Play Therapist (in the
United Kingdom) or their equivalents in other countries, is desirable to
ensure that the therapist has a solid developmental and clinical foundation
in play therapy before combining it with AAT. Simply using a dog to
play with a child during therapy sessions does not constitute therapy,
and it is potentially damaging and unethical.

Play therapists who use their own dogs must also develop dog
handling skills. This most often occurs during the canine training period.
The therapist provides a role model for the children with whom the dog
works, so the safe, smooth, and sensitive management of the dog within
the play therapy context is important. An alternative is for the play
therapist to work in conjunction with a dog handler, but this is not always
possible due to financial, privacy, or other clinical considerations. When
it is possible, the dog handler must also demonstrate a positive, respectful
relationship with the dog.

Play therapy dogs may need some training and encouragement
that differ a bit from other therapy dog training programs. Therapy dog
training is valuable, but the use of a dog during play sessions might
require a somewhat different range of skills and behaviors than dogs
used with other types of therapy.

Training needs to build on the playful nature of the dog. Many
dogs are eager to play, and others can be prompted to play by using
natural canine play postures or by enticing them with their favorite toys
or treats. Training that reinforces these play behaviors can strengthen
the likelihood that a dog will engage in play "on invitation" in a session.
Play therapy dogs can learn a variety of tricks that can be used in

conjunction with children. It is important to develop play behaviors that are already in the dog's repertoire and to use the dog's natural inclinations to develop playful interactions. For example, retrieving behaviors can be strengthened by playing ball, tossing a Frisbee, or teaching the dog to retrieve specific toys that might be in the playroom. At the same time, the therapist must avoid unintentionally provoking more instinctual behaviors that could be counterproductive. For example, if a herding dog nips at the heels of fast moving children, games involving running are best avoided unless the dog is reliably trained to refrain from those behaviors. The therapist must know the dog very well, and the play activities to be used with children must first be tried during training sessions to learn how the dog reacts.

The play therapy dog needs to learn to tolerate some confusion that occurs during play sessions, such as when the child first wants the dog to help "track down" the ghosts, and then when the child wants to tackle the ghosts alone without the help of the canine therapist, as often happens in mastery play. This can make it difficult for the dog to determine if it should join the play or not. Of course, the human play therapist can assist by calling the dog away from the child when the child says, "Now stand back. I'm going in after those ghosts myself." Also, children's sudden movements can startle animals, as can strange noises emanating from toys. The dog needs a great deal of prior exposure to all of these materials and situations, and toys that continue to cause stress for the dog should be removed. For example, some electronic toys emit an array of strange, loud sounds. Some dogs learn to accept these noises as part of the normal environment, while others may continue to be startled and worried by them. For the latter dogs, these toys should be removed. At least some of the dog's training should be completed in the actual therapy rooms and playrooms that are used with clients in order to identify and avoid these types of fear or startle reactions in the presence of children or families.

Some behaviors that are considered undesirable by other canine therapy programs might actually be beneficial during play therapy. For example, a dog who sometimes misbehaves in minor ways might provide a realistic challenge for a child who has difficulty behaving appropriately as well. The play therapist can use the dog's "misbehaviors" as a metaphor for children's difficulties, and the children can be enlisted to help the dog gain better control. Some of the methods that children use to help the dog can then be used to manage their own behavior. Other behaviors that ordinarily are discouraged in dog training but used during play therapy might include the dog's excited enthusiasm, barking, and licking. As with children, dogs can become quite excited and need to learn how to calm themselves. Children can learn ways to manage their own arousal by helping the dog. Barking can be used with a wide range of games where the dog communicates its reactions when cued. And although many people dislike licking, children often see it as a sign of affection. Any of these more rambunctious behaviors that are useful within the play therapy context must nevertheless be under the control of the therapist in order to prevent anxiety or injury to the child as well as stress in the dog.

Training the canine play therapist should involve basic obedience interspersed with play training. Because playing *is* the dog's work, it is important that the dog can switch readily from play behaviors to obedience. Play training teaches and reinforces the dog while it is engaged in an inherently enjoyable activity. For example, a dog that enjoys chasing a ball can be asked to sit-stay or down-stay prior to being released to run after the ball. A short series of throws that requires the dog to wait before chasing the ball are then followed by several throws where the dog is permitted to take off immediately as the ball leaves the human's hand. Simple gestures, verbal cues, or whistles can be used to help the dog distinguish the differences. To maintain the dog's motivation, ample play that is not restricted by commands should be interspersed.

Canine sport activities can be incorporated into play therapy. Canine agility training can be used in noncompetitive, informal ways to encourage active interaction between dog and child and to build the child's confidence (and probably the dog's as well). Any dog who has already been trained to run agility courses can be brought in for the child to play with on just part of a course, or the child can learn how to do agility training with his or her own pet. On Course for Kids (Dana Crevling, personal communication, November 15, 2006; www.dogsofcourse.com) is a unique program that enlists trained volunteer human-canine agility teams to work with child cancer patients as part of a fundraising event for the Floating Children's Cancer Center Childlife Program in Boston, Massachusetts. Funds are used for child life specialists, the playroom, materials, outings, and other types of support. The child actually joins the agility team and participates while the dogs run the course. This idea can be adapted for mental health work as well.

All types of dog training should be done several times a day for short intervals of approximately 10 minutes. Repetition with food, praise, or play rewards works best. If the dog "forgets" or fails to follow through as expected, it is most effective to ignore the error and try again later (Donaldson, 2005; Dunbar, 1996a, 1996b; Katz, 2005). Scolding rarely accomplishes anything except to make the dog more anxious. Clicker training (Pryor, 1999, 2005; Sdao, 2006) can also be beneficial for play therapy, and children often enjoy use of the clicker while learning the process. (In clicker training, the handler uses a simple hand-held metal clicker as a conditioned reinforcer. Dogs learn quickly that the click signals some tasty treats that follow. Using clickers allows handlers to provide immediate reinforcement for dog behaviors, and this training method is gaining popularity because of its effectiveness.)

Because the use of canines in play therapy is relatively new, it is expected that future training methods will be refined as play therapists find innovative ways of incorporating dogs into their work. The key is to ensure that the dog is not stressed by the training and that the training matches the temperament and individual characteristics of the dog *and* the therapist. If the dog does not enjoy the training and the work, then motivation lags and frustration and failure follow. Keeping the training process positive, fun, and attuned to the dog's needs facilitates a successful working relationship. Some examples follow.

My play therapy dog, Kirrie, has many characteristics of Border Collies – she has high energy, learns exceptionally quickly, plays and exercises endlessly, and needs to be kept busy with a "job." When we adopted her from a Border Collie rescue, I immediately noticed characteristics that suggested she would get along well with our grandchildren, and have since helped her become an effective play therapy dog. She was very friendly, tolerated lots of situations readily, and had a "soft mouth." She got along well with our other dogs, and she often engaged them and our cats in play. She seemed to have no particular "agenda" but to keep busy and to enjoy herself. She also seemed to read and react appropriately to people's moods. Her worst habits were jumping up on people, licking hands and faces excessively, and tearing paper towels into dozens of tiny pieces at a rate that would challenge the world record for speed-shredding.

Her training consists of three or four 10-minute training periods each day. This is easy as I work from a home office much of the time, and our practice in a nearby town has a generous enclosed grassy area. Kirrie requires a great deal of exercise, so training periods are usually followed by several minutes of ball play. It quickly became clear during our early training sessions that she is motivated much more by play and praise than by food when she is excited. She learns quickly and retains what she has learned as long as I continue with regular training and socialization experiences.

After basic obedience training, we worked to reduce her jumping up behaviors, and I began training to eliminate her licking. It was at this time that she first joined me in play therapy with a 13-year-old foster boy with serious trauma and attachment issues. He was so pleased that she licked him (and hence, "liked" him) that I began to rethink her training. I simultaneously realized that the licking seemed to serve calming and social interaction functions for Kirrie, and I believed that it might be unrealistic, and perhaps unkind, to expect her to eliminate it entirely. When I saw that most other children had the same positive reaction to her licking, I changed the training goal from elimination of licking to permitting some licking as long as she would stop when told "enough!" For children who dislike licking, we simply tell her "enough" as soon as she starts or redirect her to lick me for a short time.

As I began to see the possibilities of using her in conjunction with both nondirective and directive play therapy, I knew I wanted to preserve her spontaneity and joie de vivre while gaining better control of her excessive enthusiasm and energy. Although I had trained dogs before, I had never prepared a dog specifically for play therapy work, and I learned and revised my thinking as we progressed.

I was aware that some trainers and animal behaviorists draw a clear distinction between a dog's work and play, but because play *was* our work, it seemed this approach was not as relevant to our training. At times, I blended our training and our playtimes, telling Kirrie to sit-stay or to down-stay until I threw the ball and said "okay." This took effort and control on her part, as she loved to take off on an all-out run just before the ball left my hand. After several of these controlled trials, I gave her the hand signal or verbal "okay" that meant she could run out at will. This became an effective way of training and reinforcing her in a manner that was enjoyable for her. Using some of her herding instincts, I was also able to train her to run out in various directions, around objects, and other "tricks" that have been useful in therapy.

I also wanted to teach her other play activities that could be incorporated into play therapy sessions. I soon realized that her natural playfulness presented many opportunities for this. Rather than teaching her new tricks of my own devising, I watched her natural play and looked for ideas. In this way, the "hammock game" was born. With minimal training, she would bounce a ball tossed onto a rope hammock with her nose until it reached the edge and she could catch it. The hammock game eventually became a play therapy intervention about persevering when things don't come easily and also about cooperation. Children have learned how to throw and position the ball to increase Kirrie's chances of success in catching the ball within a specified number of bounces off her nose.

Another game was developed using Kirrie's inclination to keep "her people" in sight. (When walking off-leash in safe environments, she loops back regularly to ensure that we are still with her.) Her hide-and-seek game arose during a play therapy session when a child hid in an egg-shaped chair that has a fold-down fabric screen that hides the child inside. When Kirrie quickly located the child, she used her nose to raise the screen, much to the delight of the child.

Although I do not typically use our Beagles in play therapy work, I have included them occasionally. Sniffing games, especially if they involve food treats, are easy to play with them. Several traumatized children have pretended that the Beagles are search-and-rescue dogs looking for survivors of a disaster, using small treats hidden in the playroom to represent trapped survivors in need of help. Another child, after seeing a television program about Beagles used to locate contraband in airport baggage, pretended he was a drug enforcement officer with a K-9 partner sniffing for drugs. He had recently witnessed a drug-related shooting in his neighborhood. Interestingly, as I regularly played the food-sniffing game with the Beagles at home, Kirrie began participating, as well. Now she has added the "Find It" game to her play therapy repertoire.

These examples show how the dogs' natural inclinations can be used and reinforced as part of play therapy. There are countless interventions that can arise from a thoughtful observation and creative incorporation of the canine therapist's own tendencies and talents. Later sections will include interventions developed in this manner to meet the needs of children in play therapy.

PRACTICAL MANAGEMENT

When I was in fifth grade, Mr. Lester (neighbor) asked me to watch his dog Smiley. I gave Smiley a cool haircut, but my mom was really mad and grounded me.

-Donnie, 16-year-old boy

There are many ways in which play therapists can incorporate canines into their work. This section focuses on some of the options to make it work well. The suggestions here are not exhaustive, however, and the precise manner in which the therapist structures and organizes the canine's involvement may take a different form altogether. The reader is also referred to volumes on Animal-Assisted Therapy (AAT) for more details on this subject (e.g., Chandler, 2005; Delta Society, 2004; Fine, 2000, 2006; Levinson & Mallon, 1997).

OPTIONS FOR DOG HANDLING

There are two primary options for handling the dog. Play therapists serve as the handlers for their own dogs, or play therapists work in tandem with other people who bring in and handle their own therapy-trained dogs. For play therapists handling their own dogs, it is important that they augment their play therapy background with canine training and handling skills as well as knowledge and experience with AAT principles, methods, and precautions. If the play therapist works with another individual who has a background in dog handling and AAT, there are several areas that must be worked out, including confidentiality of client information and coordination of schedules. The play therapist should develop at least a basic knowledge of AAT, while the dog handler needs to understand the basic principles and methods of the play therapy approaches that are likely to be used. As the play therapist and the dog handler become more familiar with each other's fields, they will work out a partnership that will help them work efficiently and effectively together during sessions. Although the play therapist handling his or her own dog is the simplest and most common way of combining animal-assisted therapy and play therapy, the separate dog handler arrangement is a viable alternative.

CONSENT

In general, the therapist should obtain parental permission prior to any family contact with the canine play therapist. The child's history of allergies or negative interactions with dogs is obtained from the parents, as well. Once written parental consent is obtained, the therapist suggests the use of the dog to the child. At no time should the child be forced to interact with a dog.

If the dogs are always present at the office or site, then the therapist informs parents of this during the initial phone contact. Written consent should still be obtained, however, for any specific sessions held involving the dog and the child.

ALLERGIES AND ZOÖNOSES

Allergies, parasites, and diseases communicable to humans from animals (zoönoses) can pose problems for children and families interacting with therapy dogs. Individuals with suppressed immune systems sometimes experience problems as well, although many live with pets without difficulty. A clean, well-groomed dog is essential. Some dog breeds are much less likely to cause allergic reactions because they shed very little. Poodles and some mixed breeds including Poodles, such as Labradoodles (Labrador retrievers mixed with Poodles), are often used because even people with allergies can usually work with them. There are also washes and treatments available that can reduce dander and allergic reactions, but play therapists and dog handlers should consult with their veterinarians before using them on their dogs.

Effective treatments are also available to eliminate fleas, ticks, and other parasites from dogs. All therapy dogs should be kept free from these pests, and should they acquire any parasites, they should stay at home until the problem has been resolved. The same is true of illnesses. If dogs have urinary infections, diarrhea, injuries, or any other illness, they should be permitted to recover in a relaxed home environment and return to play therapy work only after they have fully recovered.

PLAYROOM SETUP

The following items are needed in the play therapy room or office:

- Water bowl and water
- Dog bed/pillow
- Blankets and towels
- Dog toys and chews (e.g., balls, long tug toys, Kongs)
- Brushes and grooming tools
- Dog treats and food
- Crate, if dog is used to one and prefers the "den" environment when relaxing
- Some dog-friendly dress-up scarves or bandannas
- Clicker, if clicker training is used.

Within the playroom, a corner should be used as the "dog's area." The dog can retreat to this area when tired or stressed, and the therapist can direct the dog to this area if the child is not asking to include the canine. Another separate, small area can be delineated where children can sit or cuddle with the dog or groom it.

The crate can be kept in the dog's corner in the playroom or in a separate location within the office. It should be placed in an area where the dog will not be disturbed or in the way, and where it can relax when not involved in play sessions.

It is also useful to have access to a long hallway, another room/office, and a private outdoor area for obedience and agility training activities.

INSURANCE

Because unexpected things can happen, it is a good idea to obtain insurance coverage. When dogs and their handlers are certified through the Delta Society (2004), for example, they are covered by the Delta Society's insurance policy, at least for many uses of the dog. Both general business insurance (for injuries) and professional liability insurance (for negative clinical outcomes) should be explored. Insurance companies vary substantially in their policies related to this.

RISK MANAGEMENT

The play therapist must *always* supervise the canine and the children when they are together. No matter how sweet, well-trained, and well-behaved the dog, the possibility exists that the dog will behave in an uncharacteristic or threatening manner, especially if it feels trapped or the need to defend itself. Furthermore, friendly dogs can accidentally injure children with their excited movements. Similarly, no matter how sweet, well-behaved, and responsible the child, the possibility exists that the child can injure the dog. Children simply do not always have the control or dog handling savvy needed, and they can inadvertently injure the dog or behave in a way that might be misunderstood by the canine, causing it to react negatively. Sometimes children cannot gauge when their touch or pressure can hurt another. The only way to avoid injury to canine or child is for the therapist to know what signals to watch for, when and how to intervene, and for the supervision to be constant. Chandler's (2005) book on AAT has an excellent, detailed chapter on risk management.

KNOWLEDGE OF THE CANINE

Throughout this monograph, the therapist's knowledge of the canine is emphasized. Even when a dog has been certified as a therapy dog and engages in safe, playful interactions with children and families, problems can still arise. It is not unusual for dogs to work better with some children than others. Sometimes they may be uncomfortable with one gender, or tall children, or children with squeaky voices, or younger children, or those with certain behavior problems. Just as children should never be pushed into working with the dog, the dog should never be pushed into working with a child with whom the dog has a negative or stressful reaction. During the training period, canines should be exposed to a very wide range of situations and people so the therapist/handler develops a clearer understanding of that particular dog. Constant monitoring for signs of canine stress should become second-nature during play sessions.

SIGNS OF CANINE STRESS

It is part of a play therapist's training to recognize when children are stressed, and it is important to keep alert for those signs when the dog is present, as well. Perhaps less well-known are the signals canines give when they are stressed or anxious. McConnell (2006), Kalnajs (2006a, 2006b), and Rugaas (2006) all provide excellent explanations and visual examples of these signs. Lip-licking, head-turning, nose-licking, freezing, yawning, tense or high tail-wagging, and various features of the eyes are just a few of the signs that dogs display when anxious. Even long-term dog owners are not usually familiar with some of these signs, and it is very important to learn them all. Ultimately, it is critical to watch the entire body of the dog to read its signals accurately. This is a skill that is easily acquired with proper information and regular, careful observation of the dog. Furthermore, play therapists using canines should monitor for signs of stress, not only when the dog is with children, but also when it returns home after a day's work. Donaldson (2005) explains how stressors can accumulate, erupting in never-seen-before aggressive, self-protective behavior, and her discussion of bite-thresholds is must-reading for therapists using dogs in their work.

AMOUNT OF WORK FOR THE CANINE

Play therapy dogs should work only as much as they seem to enjoy without becoming stressed. The extent of the dog's working schedule depends on the nature of the work as well as on the dog itself.

The nature of the canine's work within the play therapy office is an important determinant of the amount of involvement. If the dog is simply present in the office, with just an occasional play session or intervention, then it may adjust to being there on a full-time basis. Much like a "shop dog," this canine greets people and occasionally interacts with them, but spends much of its time napping or in other canine pursuits. If the dog is working regularly in play sessions, however, with children "training" and interacting with it, a part-time schedule might be more appropriate for the dog.

The canine's interest, energy level, and stamina should be used to determine the best schedule. For some dogs, it might be just a few hours each week, whereas for others it might be a few days per week. Some play therapists have more than one trained therapy dog so that they can work in play sessions regularly but have half-days or alternating days off.

Adequate time needs to be built into the play therapy schedule for canine bathroom breaks and naps. Play therapists should remember that dogs naturally spend much time sleeping, and knowing the rhythms of the dog's energy levels and playfulness helps determine the amount of work that can reasonably be expected. If play therapists use the services of several different handlers of therapy dogs, then greater coverage of session time is possible. This option requires that the play therapist invest more time and effort in developing collaborative relationships with the handlers, however.

DEGREE OF CANINE INVOLVEMENT
WITHIN THE CHILD'S TREATMENT PLAN

Canine play therapy is likely to be one component of a more comprehensive treatment plan for any child. The degree of involvement depends on several factors. First, the frequency of canine play therapy sessions depends on the specific treatment goals set for the child, and the extent that the dog plays a role in accomplishing them. Some children are likely to benefit more from canine play therapy sessions than others. Second, the dog's energy, stamina, and apparent enjoyment of the work in general and with specific children are other limiting factors. Third, the demand for the canine play therapist's services also impacts the degree to which the dog is used with any individual. If the dog's services must be stretched to benefit many children, then the frequency with which it works with any particular child might be reduced. Fourth, although dogs might be present for every session of some children, they need not be used for each entire session, and they can often be used during every second or third session if necessary. Some regularity of involvement is needed for continuity, but alternating canine play therapy sessions with other interventions that do not use the dog seem to work well for both child and canine. Preliminary results from Thompson's (2007) study of dogs in nondirective play therapy suggest, however, that some children clearly miss the dog when it is not present.

CANINES AND COUNTERTRANSFERENCE

Finally, some self-monitoring on the part of the play therapist is needed. Because therapists often have close, attached relationships with their pets, they may react negatively to children or families who are uninterested in the therapy animal or who express distaste for the dog. Protective feelings may arise when children try to treat the dog badly, and these can color the therapist's future attitudes toward those clients. As with all countertransference, the therapist needs to monitor negative feelings that arise in conjunction with the use of the dog, evaluate the sources of those reactions, and discuss them with a supervisor or other colleague if they do no dissipate rapidly. Therapists might choose to end their use of the dog with some children and families, but if negative attitudes toward the child or family linger, then consultation with a colleague is indicated.

THE FIRST MEETING:
PREPARATIONS AND INTRODUCTIONS

*She likes me **a lot**! Can she play with me every time?*
　　　　　-Jasmine, 6-year-old girl, when meeting Kirrie

Most children are excited about meeting the therapist's play therapy dog. There are several preliminary steps to ensure that the child's interactions with the dog are safe and positive. Even when the play therapy dog has a suitable temperament and is well trained for this work, children can be unpredictable. This section covers some basic advance preparations useful for children as well as ways the therapist can structure the initial meeting with the dog.

IS THIS MODALITY APPROPRIATE FOR THE CHILD AND THE CANINE?

The therapist needs to make an initial determination if the use of the play therapy dog is appropriate for each child. This is usually done in conjunction with the parent or caregiver. The therapist needs to determine if the child has allergies or past behavior problems that might be contraindications for canine play therapy. Much of this information can be gathered routinely during intake interviews with parents prior to the child's attendance at therapy. Some of the key questions are below:

- Does your child have a history of allergies to dogs or other animals? If so, what restrictions must be followed?
- What types of prior experiences has the child had with animals, and dogs in particular? Are there animals in the family home? How does the child feel about them and interact with them?
- Has the child ever attempted to hurt an animal? If so, what are the details? Has this happened more than once?
- Is the child afraid of dogs?
- Does the child have aggressive tendencies or has the child routinely been disrespectful of objects or people? Does the child have a tendency to hit or bite when frustrated?
- How well does the child listen to and comply with parents and other authority figures?

Affirmative answers to any of these questions would not necessarily rule out the use of canines in play therapy, but they might. They might also determine the timing of canine interventions as well as the nature of them. An example follows.

Sonny was a 7-year-old boy with conduct problems. He was severely oppositional with his parents, teachers, and other adults. When he was 5 years old, he had been physically injured and emotionally traumatized in a car accident, and his family reported feeling "guilty" whenever they disciplined him. There were no pets in the family home, but he had pulled the tail of his grandmother's cat and dumped a small bucket of water on the cat. The therapist did not immediately use the canine in sessions, but started with several play sessions until she could evaluate the child further. She incorporated the play therapy dog after four play sessions, as she felt it could help the child with his behavior problems as well as his potentially hurtful ways of interacting with animals. She involved the dog in structured ways to ensure the safety of everyone involved. A gradual process was used to help the boy learn to enjoy the dog in an appropriate manner. The dog's involvement directly addressed the boy's tendencies to hurt pets, and it indirectly helped him with his conduct problems.

A therapist should *never* leave any child alone with a therapy dog. Continuous therapist supervision of child-dog interactions is necessary for the safety of both child and dog. Having knowledge of the child's history with pets helps the therapist make informed choices about the ways in which to involve the therapy dog with the child.

CHILD PREPARATION

In most cases, the therapist tells the child about the therapy dog, shows a photo, and asks if the child would like to meet the dog. Children should always have a choice about whether to work with the dog. The therapist shares some simple background information about the dog, such as name, breed or breed combinations, age, and anything else that might interest the child.

Some children have had prior experiences with family or neighborhood dogs, while others may have had little chance to interact with dogs or may even fear them. Although properly trained therapy dogs are tolerant of a wide range of child behaviors, including fast or unexpected movements, it is still advisable to give children brief training on how to approach and meet a dog.

McConnell (2002, 2005) has thoroughly described how humans, as members of the primate family, approach and introduce themselves in very different ways than canines do. When children meet dogs, they quite naturally approach them from the front, look them straight in the eye, pat them on the head, and wrap their arms around their necks. All of these behaviors, in canine body language, can signal aggression. Many children are bitten each year, often in the face, because of their primate approach to a canine.

Even though therapy dogs are trained to tolerate these approaches, it is beneficial for the therapist to teach children a safer way to greet the dog prior to their first meeting. This helps children learn to watch for dogs' behavioral signals, helps children take some of the responsibility for a friendly introduction, and provides children with canine-friendly greeting behaviors that they can use with dogs they meet in their daily lives, as well. There are a number of useful resources on this topic (Kalnajs, 2006b; McConnell, 2002, 2005; Rugaas, 2006). The "Be a Tree" approach (Pelar, 2005; www.doggonesafe.com) is useful to include in the child's early repertoire. It helps children assume the posture of a tree, standing still with their arms (branches) drawn in with hands folded in front and looking at their feet (roots). This gives children something concrete to do that can prevent bites from unfamiliar dogs and helps them feel in control of their own safety.

The therapist can provide this preparatory training in a very playful manner. Using a stuffed toy dog to demonstrate and practice can add to the fun as well as to the child's skill development. The therapist first demonstrates how children can stand still with hands at their sides or in front and allow the dog to approach and sniff them, or how to walk up to a dog at an angle or from the side rather than straight-on. After the dog sniffs a bit and seems comfortable, the child can offer to pet or scratch the dog on the chest or under the chin. The therapist can explain that most dogs prefer this type of greeting and will really feel safe and like the child if scratched from below rather than above. The therapist encourages the child to try it with the toy dog, praises the child's efforts in the right direction, and then helps the child apply this approach when meeting the therapy dog.

To maintain children's interest, the preliminary training should be brief, but it can be useful to teach children some of the very basic obedience cues prior to meeting the therapy dog or soon thereafter. Verbal and hand cues such as *Look* (to ask the dog to look at the child's face), *Come, Sit, Stay, Down, Off,* and *Good* might be useful starting cues. Again, if the therapist teaches these cues in a playful manner, the children will not feel performance pressure and are more likely to learn them. For example, one way to help younger children learn the cues is by "playing dog" with them. After explaining the cues, the therapist invites children to pretend they are dogs who follow the cues the therapist gives them. The therapist praises the children (as if they were dogs) in a playful manner, and then reverses roles, asking the children to give the cues to the therapist who now plays the dog. This lighthearted game quickly teaches the cues to children, preparing them for use with the actual dog (VanFleet, 2008).

If training treats are used with the dog, the therapist should show children how to use them, as well. Children can either sprinkle the treats on the floor when meeting the dog or else hold them in the open palm of the hand for the dog to lick out. To avoid unintentional nips or bites, children generally should not hold treats pinched between their fingers.

> I spent 10 minutes preparing 7-year-old Trisha to meet Kirrie. Trisha had a pet dog at home, but she had not been around dogs as large as Kirrie before. For practice, I used an 18 inch tall stuffed toy Beagle that is posed in a sitting position. As I explained the approach, I demonstrated it on the stuffed toy Beagle, then asked her to try it with the toy. We both laughed and smiled as we practiced. When she stroked the Beagle's chest, I made happy-sounding dog noises to keep the atmosphere playful and to reinforce her efforts. Then as she tried the "Come" cue, I picked up the dog and pretended to have it run to her. Then she said, "Good doggie!" Laughing along with her, I told her, "That's just the way to do it!" We then decided to meet Kirrie, and she used the skills we had just covered, with encouragement and just a few suggestions from me during the actual meeting.

INTRODUCING CHILD AND DOG

The therapist needs to establish a relaxed atmosphere for the initial meeting. This helps both the child and the dog feel comfortable. The therapist has a great deal of responsibility at this meeting, needing to ensure that safety is preserved for all involved and that the meeting is a positive experience for child and dog. It would be understandable if the therapist felt some anxiety, but canines pick up on handler anxiety quickly, and their own anxiety can increase. To establish a calm, friendly environment, the therapist must dispel his or her own anxiety and relax. These meetings are often pleasant and heartwarming, and they can be an enjoyable therapeutic experience.

If the dog is on a lead, it should be held loosely. The methods of greeting taught to the child previously are used with the actual therapy dog. The child stands still and lets the dog approach, rubs the dog's chest or chin, and/or sprinkles treats on the floor. The therapist should refrain from overcontrolling the meeting verbally, as well. Short suggestions to the child and praise for both the therapy dog and the child are helpful; detailed instructions and corrections are not.

> Nathan was a 14-year-old foster child with impulse control problems. He was very excited about meeting Kirrie. His preliminary training immediately preceded his actual meeting with the dog. Nathan waited in the playroom while Kirrie entered. He stood still while she immediately came up to him, and then he tossed a small handful of training treats on the floor. Kirrie wagged her entire back end and sniffed his shoes. I told Kirrie to sit and stay, and then Nathan walked to her side and reached down and scratched her chest. I crouched down next to both of them. I commented, "Look how much she likes you! She can barely sit still because she's still wagging her tail. She sure likes that chest scratching. You're doing just great. She can't wait to play with you." I also spoke to Kirrie, praising her sit-stay, and saying, "Kirrie, Nathan really is being nice with you, isn't he? He's knows just how to make you feel good!" After this initial greeting, we moved into other play therapy activities that involved Kirrie.

CANINE COTHERAPISTS IN NONDIRECTIVE AND DIRECTIVE PLAY THERAPY

The dog was created specially for children. He is the god of frolic.
-Henry Ward Beecher

The field of play therapy has often been described as being comprised of two major categories, nondirective play therapy and directive play therapy. The essential difference lies in who chooses the type of play that takes place. In nondirective play therapy, also known as Child-Centered Play Therapy (CCPT) in the United States (Landreth, 2002; VanFleet, 2006a; Wilson & Ryan, 2005), the therapist sets a climate of safety and acceptance and then allows the child to select what to play with and how to play with it. It arises from the theoretical assumptions and orientation of humanistic (Rogerian) psychology. The therapist believes in children's ability to solve many of their own problems if given the proper atmosphere of safety and acceptance, and then follows the child's lead. In directive play therapies, the therapist makes the initial choice of toys or activities for the session (Kaduson et al., 1997; Kaduson & Schaefer, 2000, 2006), based upon theoretical orientation, an assessment of the child's needs, and treatment goals. Directive play therapies represent many different theoretical orientations. Many play therapists are trained in a wide range of approaches and use both nondirective and directive play therapy approaches with children, although usually not simultaneously, as the child could become confused by the different underlying assumptions. Quality play therapy, whether nondirective or directive, is closely attuned to the child's strengths, needs, and motivations and uses play in a systematic manner to facilitate therapeutic and developmental change. Canine play therapists can be involved in either of these broad categories of play therapy.

CANINES IN NONDIRECTIVE PLAY THERAPY

> *A dog doesn't care if you're rich or poor, big or small, young or old. He doesn't care if you're not smart, not popular, not a good joke-teller, not the best athlete, not the best-looking person. To your dog, you are the greatest, the smartest, the nicest human being who was ever born. You are his friend and protector.*
> -Louis Sabin *(All About Dogs as Pets)*

Because dogs are often viewed as accepting and nonjudgmental, they can easily be incorporated into nondirective, or child-centered, play sessions. A small section of the playroom, preferably a corner, is turned into the dog's area, with a bed, grooming supplies, a few dog toys, and possibly some bones or chews that are safe for dogs to eat and for children to handle. This provides the dog with an area in which to relax when it chooses, or when the child seems uninterested in involving the dog.

The therapist conducts the play session much as any other CCPT session, and the dog becomes one more "object" with which the child may choose to play. This is similar to the human play therapist's role, which is to be present and accepting of the child, and to become involved directly in the play only when the child invites the therapist to do so.

The child decides the level of both the human and canine therapists' involvement. A dog used in CCPT must be trained well enough to take a back seat if necessary, to sit on the sidelines until told otherwise. Prior training in long down-stays can be helpful, or the dog can be directed to its corner and signaled to lie down, where it can amuse itself with its own toys, chewies, or naps.

When the child plays in a more solitary manner and does not involve the dog or the therapist in roles within imaginative play, the therapist provides empathic listening responses to the child, and sometimes delivers statements of the child's feelings to the dog, such as "Janie is really busy in that kitchen today, Kirrie. She's having a lot of fun cooking things" or "Phil is having a tough time battling those bad guys, Kirrie. They sure look mean and nasty, but he keeps getting back up to fight them. He really wants to conquer them." The tracking responses common to CCPT can also be delivered as a third-person narration to the dog, with the feelings inserted: "Now the wizard is waving her wand. It looks like she's casting a spell. Oh, Kirrie! The wizard just turned the boy into a frog! She thinks that's funny."

Mary Thompson (2007; personal communication, December 12, 2006), one of the pioneers in blending AAT with play therapy, has described the use of her two TDI-certified Shetland Sheepdogs in her nondirective play sessions:

> I introduce the therapy dog to the child from the first play session. I read the child a book about play therapy and immediately engage the therapy dog by pretending the dog is also involved in the storytelling, in much the same way as using a puppet to talk to the child. The dog shows the child to the playroom after we explain the purpose of play sessions and after the child has been introduced to the therapy dog. The child is given a tour of the playroom and is also shown an area known as the "Cozy Corner." This is an area dedicated to child-animal interaction. The corner includes the dog's toys, a large pillow for the two of them to sit on, stories for the child to read to the dog, and a brush the child can use on the dog. Children are introduced to this area in the same way they are introduced to all of the other toys in the fully stocked playroom.
>
> While in the playroom the therapy dog is an active part of the session. I often make tracking statements to the therapy dog instead of directly to the child. I have found this incorporates another living being into the session and allows the child to better accept the tracking of feelings and behaviors. For example, I may say to the therapy dog,

"Johnny is having a hard time deciding what he wants to play with next," or "Johnny seems frustrated with those things today." Tracking statements can also come directly from the dog. For example, I may say to a child, "Razz (therapy dog) notices that you are very angry." Often children respond better to tracking when it is coming from the dog than from me.

I use most of the nondirective play therapy strategies but allow the dog to have a voice in the session. What physical contact and activities the dog does with the child is completely up to the child. I do not plan specific activities for them to do together although I let the children know from the beginning what activities they are able to do with the dog. These include obedience or agility training, playing fetch, petting, talking, reading, or grooming the dog. The dog becomes a part of their therapy and they expect his or her presence at each session. Given that I have multiple dogs, many children often schedule their appointments on certain days to ensure their "favorite dog" is present.

Sometimes children involve the human or canine therapist in roles in their imaginary play. In CCPT, the human play therapist tries to follow the child's lead by playing the imaginary role as the child wants. The therapist then becomes an actor in the play, using "faces" and "voices" or donning costumes to play the dramatic role as the child wishes. In a similar way, the therapist helps the dog play roles requested by the child, as long as those roles are safe and the dog is willing to play along. The human therapist's role is to facilitate the interaction so that the canine's involvement comes close to what the child desires. An example follows.

Nine-year-old Kelly pretended she was a teacher at school. She wanted Kirrie to play her student. I gave Kirrie the signal to sit and stay while Kelly "taught" her some spelling words. Kelly then asked Kirrie to "raise her hand in class." I had not yet taught Kirrie to raise her paw or do anything like this, so I sat next to Kirrie and manually raised her paw for a few seconds. When Kirrie seemed uncomfortable with this, I then raised my own hand, which I held right next to Kirrie's foreleg as if it were Kirrie's. Kelly readily accepted this "pretend" enactment of what she wanted, and then moved to something else in her play.

Many times, children choose roles for the dog that are more canine in nature, such as the child's pet dog, a search-and-rescue dog, a show dog, a bomb-sniffing dog, or a police officer's K-9 partner. Sometimes children want to play a dog themselves and interact with the actual canine as if they were pack-mates. If a child wants the dog to do something that might be harmful or stressful for the dog, the therapist simply sets a limit on that particular behavior and redirects the child in a general manner, as was done for a young "cowboy" who began to put his leg over Kirrie's back as if she were a horse, "You'd like to ride Kirrie, but one of the rules is that you may not sit on Kirrie or put your leg over her back. You can do just about anything else, though."

Although interruptions and diversions sometimes occur, the therapist tries to follow the basic principles and methods of nondirective play therapy as much as possible. Children quickly learn the appropriate ways of including the dog in their play, if they so choose, and there are rarely problems that cannot be handled with the usual nondirective play therapy skills.

Canines can be integrated into nondirective play therapy to address a wide range of child problem areas. Although the sections that follow describe specific directive canine-assisted play therapy methods to address certain problems, nondirective play therapy with a dog can be used for nearly all the problem areas addressed, either exclusively or in conjunction with some of the directive approaches.

CANINES IN DIRECTIVE PLAY THERAPY

Canines can be used in a wide range of directive play therapy interventions. Because the therapist is more involved in designing and introducing activities for the child, it is relatively easy to add a canine component. The therapist structures the session to include the dog in part or all of the intervention. When including a dog, the therapist thinks first about the child's needs and then about how some of the dog's capabilities might help meet those needs. Directive play therapy activities can include training, storytelling, fantasy play, and games. The therapist can also weave spontaneous events between the child and dog into new interventions. Sometimes the dog is simply present in the room while the child is involved in a project or activity, such as painting or sandtray, and at other times the dog is an integral part of the intervention. Much of the rest of this monograph includes a wide range of directive play therapy approaches that includes canines.

THERAPEUTIC POWERS OF PLAY

The "therapeutic powers of play" (Schaefer, 1993) can provide a template for the use of a dog in both nondirective and directive forms of play therapy. These therapeutic powers are operative inherently through the structure and acceptance of nondirective play therapy, whereas in directive modalities, the therapist can devise canine-assisted activities that harness the therapeutic powers of play to address the child's problems. The therapeutic powers most relevant to more directive forms of canine play therapy are briefly described below. In each of these arenas, the therapist incorporates the dog in *playful* ways. Rarely are these subjects discussed seriously with children. Play therapy, with or without a dog involved, is effective because its playful nature keeps therapeutic work emotionally safe for children. More specific ideas and detailed examples of each of these follow in subsequent sections.

Overcoming Resistance. Even the most resistant children seem to be disarmed by the presence of a therapy dog. Their resistance to therapy often arises from their fears of the unknown (therapy), prior negative experiences with adults or authority figures, or their need to defend themselves in real or imagined ways. Many children are surprised and delighted to find a dog at the therapist's office. The mere presence of the dog is often enough to engage the child and to alter the child's perceptions of the therapist. Children seem more likely to accept that "any adult who would have a dog here must be okay," or "the therapist seems to trust me with his or her own dog, so maybe this will be different from other experiences I've had."

Communication. Because play is a strong form of expression for children and dogs alike, it can be incorporated into many play therapy activities. The therapist can encourage the child to communicate verbally with the dog, by telling it stories, worries, or almost anything relevant to the child's or dog's life. Nonverbal expression is also easy through the use of hand signals, petting, grooming, calming signals, and body postures.

Emotional Awareness and Regulation. Children can learn to watch the dog's facial and body expressions to determine how the dog is feeling. Feeling interpretations are most effective when kept simple: Does the dog seem happy or sad? Is it angry or excited? It is not unusual in canine-assisted play therapy for children who have been referred because of their insensitivity to others' feelings to become very concerned about the dog's well-being. This permits children to expand their awareness of emotions in a variety of situations. The act of playing helps children release stress and access greater enjoyment and happiness in their lives. Play therapy dogs simply provide an interesting alternative format for these same things. Finally, when children are playing with the therapy dog, the therapist can help them learn to manage the dog's, and consequently, their own, levels of arousal.

Facilitation of Learning. Children learn best when they are enjoying the process. Canine play therapists can help children enjoy a wide range of activities. Canine reading programs help children learn to read better and with less anxiety. When children "teach" the dog new tricks or learn to train the dog, they are developing their own capacities to learn new things as well. Children with more tactile or kinesthetic learning styles might also benefit because interacting and playing with a dog usually involves considerable contact and movement.

Power and Control. Through their play, children are able to express powerful motivations relating to power and control. Because children are not permitted much power in their daily lives at home or school, they often play out themes of power and control. Play sessions give them a chance to explore these areas without risk of getting in trouble. When dogs are incorporated into the process, children can learn appropriate, safe ways to manage their own and the dog's behavior.

Role Play and Behavioral Change. Children frequently and spontaneously engage in dramatic roles during play therapy. They sometimes ask the dog or the human therapist to enact a role with them. In directive play therapy, the therapist can suggest dramatic play with the dog that will address specific behavioral issues of the child.

Stimulation of Development. Because play is the primary means through which children develop socially, emotionally, cognitively, physically, and behaviorally, play therapy fosters healthy development. Canine play therapy assists this process. Because children are drawn to animals nearly as much as they are drawn to play, the combination of these areas of natural child interest facilitates a wide range of developmental processes.

Stress Management. Playing releases stress. Playing with a dog also releases stress. Furthermore, children can learn relaxation through canine-assisted play therapy. For example, children can help the therapy dog and themselves relax through petting or grooming activities. Others lean against the dog or curl up with the dog. Dogs live in the here-and-now, and children can focus on the present and set aside worries about the past or the future when playing with them.

Desensitization. Children who are afraid of dogs can overcome their fears through gradual exposure to a friendly, playful dog. Children can also overcome other fears if they have their "faithful protector" – the dog – by their side, even when they are facing those fears symbolically in the playroom.

Ego Control. When children are playing with a canine play therapist, they must be considerate, behave responsibly, focus on the dog, and plan ahead. Various canine interactions can help them reduce their impulsivity and take responsibility for their own and the dog's safety. Playing with the dog provides the motivation they need to accomplish better self-control and self-confidence. Successful experiences interacting with the dog can provide a frame of reference that the child can then use in other situations.

Problem Solving. Children encounter and resolve many problems in the playroom. The problems may seem small, such as how to make the toys work, or they may be significant and symbolic, such as how to conquer the "bad guys" who keep attacking. Children use and develop problem-solving abilities during play therapy, and a willing dog can easily be incorporated into this type of play. At times, children may need to find ways to encourage the dog to behave in a certain way, and this requires problem solving on their parts as well.

Mastery. As children gain ego strength and problem-solving skills, they overcome problems. The accepting and playful presence of a dog can give children encouragement toward this end. In addition, as children learn some basic obedience or trick training with the dog, their confidence grows. For some children, even learning how to interact with a dog is a huge accomplishment, especially if they have not encountered live animals before or if they have a history of maltreating animals.

Social Interaction and Relationship Enhancement. This benefit of play is perhaps the most relevant to canine-assisted play therapy. Play therapy dogs provide countless opportunities for children to learn social interaction skills, to attach to another living being in a safe and healthy manner, and to participate in a developing relationship. The therapist uses children's motivation to play with the dog to help the child experience and return empathy, share and take turns, and think of another's needs while deferring one's own. The human-canine relationship is primarily one of attachment, and children learn the reciprocity that is inherent in healthy human attachments and relationships. Dogs do not judge or talk back, and they seem endlessly willing to accept people. Developing trust and relationship with a canine can provide the experience and skills needed to help children take the next step toward developing better human relationships. The social lubricant effect of relationships with dogs can be carried over into human relationships, especially if facilitated by the therapist.

When using canines in conjunction with directive play therapy interventions, the therapist is encouraged to use a relatively "light touch." Although the therapist might suggest activities for the child to use with the dog, care should be taken to avoid controlling the interaction any more than is necessary to ensure safety and to support the process. Interactions between children and dogs tend to follow their own intriguing path, and sometimes the most effective role the therapist can play is to permit this to happen. Too much control or intervention removes the playfulness and interferes with relationship development between child and dog, and ultimately between child and therapist.

The sections that follow provide more detailed descriptions of how dogs can be incorporated into play therapy in ways that effectively use these powers of play. While the sections are organized by specific problem areas, the canine-assisted play therapy interventions described in each can be used with a wide range of child difficulties. For example, the ideas presented for confidence-building are likely to be useful for children with attachment or attention problems. Canine-assisted play therapy interventions used for weight reduction, such as agility, can also build children's confidence and emotional and behavioral regulation.

With any therapy, the treatment plan often blends a variety of ideas and interventions tailored to the specific needs of the child. As with play therapy in general, nondirective and directive forms of canine play therapy can be used with the same child, but they should be conducted at separate times and preferably in different rooms or environments to avoid confusing both the dog and the child with the different assumptions and principles guiding each. Finally, while this monograph on canine-assisted play therapy focuses on its use with children, many of these same principles and methods can be used effectively with families and adults.

ANXIETY REDUCTION

> *I sure know how to make dogs relax!*
> -Deena, an anxious 4-year-old girl

Children and families coping with a variety of anxiety problems can benefit from the use of canines in play therapy. Play therapy is useful in reducing anxiety. Similarly, studies of the human-animal bond and animal-assisted therapy have shown that experiences with animals can relieve anxiety for children and adults. These two therapeutic modalities can be combined to use the therapeutic benefits of each to help anxious children.

FEAR OF DOGS

Significant numbers of children have a fear of dogs. Although some of these fears are based on prior negative interactions with dogs, many children's fears appear to arise from parents' repeated warnings about dogs (Jalongo, 2004). When parents, intending to keep their children safe, show their own anxiety about canines with numerous warnings or emotional interventions when dogs are nearby, they can easily transmit this anxiety to children. Regardless of origin, children's fear of dogs can be alleviated by educating and training children on how to behave with both familiar and unknown canines, and playful interactions can desensitize children for future encounters with dogs.

Sometimes the presence of small dogs in a play therapy practice is enough to begin the process. Small dogs feel "safer" to some children, and when children have opportunities to interact with them during play therapy, it opens the door for the therapist to use other approaches to help with their fear. For example, Heidi Kaduson (personal communication, December 9, 2006) uses three Chihuahuas in conjunction with her play therapy work. The dogs are friendly and in the office all the time. Children have the option of interacting with them, and often children with fears of dogs spontaneously ask to do so. In another intervention, Heidi Kaduson (personal communication, December 9, 2006) uses one of the Chihuahuas who makes a funny grumbling noise when his belly is rubbed. She holds the dog and invites the child to talk with the dog and ask it yes-or-no questions. The therapist then strokes the dog's belly to elicit an "answer." This process seems to desensitize some children's fears as they are able to communicate with the dog in a safe environment.

Play therapy dogs can also be used as part of a more traditional desensitization procedure. The therapy dog initially "writes a letter" to the child, introducing itself in a friendly manner. The letter is personalized for both the dog and the child. A sample is included in Appendix A, page 123. After reading and showing the dog's letter, the therapist urges the child to respond briefly to the dog via a note or a message passed along to the dog by the therapist. No physical contact with the dog is used at this point.

At the next level of exposure, the therapist shares another letter from the dog, this time including a photo of the therapy dog and more information. Eventually, the therapist asks the child to provide an article of clothing, or asks the child to rub a piece of fabric on his or her arm. The therapist explains to the child that the play therapy dog will sniff the fabric and this will help the getting-acquainted process. The therapist also asks the child to provide a photo, takes a photo of the child during the session, or asks the child to draw a picture of himself or herself that can be shown to the dog.

The next phase of the desensitization involves the playful preparation of the child as described earlier. The playfulness of the process provides the relaxation that competes with the child's anxiety when thinking about being near a dog. If further relaxation is needed, the therapist uses Kaduson's (2006; Kaduson & Schaefer, 2006) bubble-blowing technique with the child. The technique is a play-based version of deep breathing exercises using soap bubbles. Using high quality soap bubbles, the therapist shows the child how to blow large bubbles by taking in a deep breath and then blowing out slowly. A playful competition ensues in which the therapist encourages the child and ensures the child's success. The child "practices" the bubble-blowing technique at home with parents in preparation for using it when first meeting the dog.

The child is likely at this point to be ready to meet the dog, but if needed, an additional step where the child sees the dog from a distance can be inserted. The child then meets the dog for a short period of time, and the therapist ensures that the interaction feels safe for the child and remains playful and friendly. The therapist models relaxed, playful interactions with the dog and the child. The length of interactions is gradually extended, and the therapy dog participates more fully in nondirective and/or directive play sessions as the child feels more comfortable.

It should be noted that all of these steps may not be necessary to desensitize many children. Often, children can be introduced to the dog relatively quickly and then given control over how close they come. Nondirective play therapy with a canine cotherapist can be useful as well because children are given control over the level of involvement of the dog in their play.

> Samantha was an 8-year-old girl who had been told repeatedly by her mother to stay away from dogs. Her mother admitted that she had been afraid of dogs after being bitten herself as a child. Samantha became agitated in the presence of all dogs, and she refused to visit friends' homes if they had pet dogs. Her mother didn't want her social interactions to be limited in this way, nor did she want Samantha to continue to have this fear as she had experienced. Kirrie introduced herself to Samantha by letter. Samantha loved receiving this letter and began asking questions about Kirrie. I asked her if she wanted to write down some of her questions for Kirrie to answer, and she did. The following week, Kirrie had "written" her answers to Samantha's questions, and Samantha brought in a school picture for me to show Kirrie. I also took a small piece of cotton, explaining how dogs always like to get a sniff of their new friends, and how this would help Kirrie feel more comfortable with her when they met. We rubbed the cotton on her arms, and I took it to share with Kirrie when I got home.
>
> The following week, I held a half-hour play session with Samantha, then spent 10 minutes showing her how to approach Kirrie when they met. Kirrie was waiting in my office. I brought Kirrie into the playroom, and Samantha asked that Kirrie stay across the room. Kirrie was wagging her tail, and I said, "I think she recognizes you

from your scent and your picture and all that I've been telling her about you. Wow, she really likes you – what do you think?" Samantha responded, "I think she likes me, too." I asked her how she could tell and she replied, "Her tail is wagging a lot!" Within minutes, Samantha asked if she could touch Kirrie. As we had prepared, Samantha rubbed Kirrie's chest and Kirrie licked her arm. Samantha hesitated at this unexpected gesture, and then giggled, "She really, really likes me!" I then suggested that she feel how soft Kirrie's ears were. Samantha did so, and we ended the session. Samantha asked if she could see Kirrie next week.

When she arrived for her next session, Samantha immediately asked if I had remembered to bring Kirrie. She was eager to play with her again, which she did near the end of the session. From that point on, Samantha had little fear of Kirrie and welcomed interactions with her. Samantha quickly mastered the skills for approaching dogs, and after three sessions with Kirrie announced that she was going to the home of one of her friends who had a miniature Schnauzer. She reported the following week that Buttons the Schnauzer really liked her, too, and that she had rubbed his chest just like Kirrie's. Improvement continued rapidly from that point forward. We included one session in which Samantha's mother joined us and Samantha taught her what she had learned about meeting and playing with dogs. Even her mother was able to relax once she saw Samantha's delight in playing with Kirrie, and although she was a bit hesitant about touching Kirrie herself, she eventually followed Samantha's lead and stroked the dog's ears. Both Samantha and her mother felt good about their courage in making a new canine friend.

OTHER ANXIETY PROBLEMS

The greatest pleasure of a dog is that you may make a fool of yourself with him, and not only will he not scold you, but he will make a fool of himself, too.
                                                            -Samuel Butler

Anxiety problems manifest in many ways in children. When children have generalized anxiety problems, sometimes the presence of a dog during play sessions can be calming in itself. Studies have shown that children who interact with dogs can have decreases in their blood pressure and stress response (Friedmann et al., 1983; Jenkins, 1986; Kaminski, Pellino, & Wish, 2002; Wells, 1998), and canines have been shown to have social lubricant effects with children (Jalongo, 2004; McNicholas & Collis, 2000, 2006; Melson, 2001; Messent, 1983). Although children's reactions are only now being studied specifically in the play therapy setting (Thompson, 2007), it seems likely that the presence of a dog can help children feel more at ease with the play therapist as well as provide a means by which children can relax during play therapy. Finally, play therapy dogs can help children become less self-conscious as their attention is focused outside themselves on the dog or the process. In a survey of the use of animals in play therapy, VanFleet (2007b) found that 84% of the responding play therapists cited rapport-building, relaxation, and social lubricant effects as a benefit of using animals, and especially dogs, in play therapy.

Anxious children sometimes present as very serious, perfectionistic, and parentified. Their focus is on themselves, and they often worry about past, present, and future events. Play therapy is beneficial for these children because it helps them release some of their anxiety and become freer to be themselves within the therapeutic process (VanFleet, 1997). Play therapy can be challenging to initiate, however, because some of these children have difficulty accessing their playful or humorous selves. Some anxious children dislike anyone watching their play, or they resist play therapy as being "for babies" or simply not intellectual enough for them. Often, these children reside in families where one or more parents report anxiety problems as well, and an atmosphere of anxiety surrounds family activities and interactions. Sometimes the pressures to do well in school and extracurricular activities are extreme (Elkind, 2007a, 2007b; Ginsburg, 2007; VanFleet, 1997). So although play therapy can be very beneficial in individual and family formats, it can sometimes be difficult to engage extremely anxious children.

Play therapy dogs can be used to help such children relax and play more spontaneously. Focus shifts from the child to the dog, and it seems that children feel less "scrutinized." In the author's clinical experience, over 90% of children who show anxiety and resistance to play therapy immediately become interested and engaged when introduced to the therapy dog. This clinical finding is consistent with the research (Gonski, 1985).

One approach to help children relax is to teach the child how to play games with the dog. This can include games of fetch or ball –

whatever the dog enjoys. The therapist can add an additional sense of fun by training the dog to respond to unconventional verbal cues that resonate with children, such as "Play ball!" or "Batter up!"

When involving the canine and child in games, the therapist points out how the dog is enjoying its interaction with the child and how free the dog seems to feel. The therapist can also mention how dogs seem to live in the present, without excessive worry about the past or the future, while engaging children in activities that help them do the same. Another approach is to teach the dog some silly tricks in which the children can take part (Bielakiewicz, 2005; Langbehn, 2003; Ludwig, 1996; Ray & Harding, 2005; Rock, 1998; Rosenthal, 1999). Such games should be based on the dog's natural inclinations, considering its personality. The therapist capitalizes on these tricks for use within play therapy.

Another technique that can be used with anxious children is the play bow. Dogs invite other dogs, and even other species, to play with them by using a characteristic posture called the play bow. The entire front end is lowered to the floor while the hips and rear of the dog remain elevated. Sometimes the dog bounces or gives short barks while in this posture, and sometimes it wriggles its hips. Its ears are pricked forward in an expression that appears to be anticipation. Most children recognize this posture as a "doggie invitation to play," and if they do not, they can be shown photos of a play bow (VanFleet, 2006b). Bekoff (2006) has written a simple, effective article in *Ranger Rick* about canine social interactions that includes the play bow and its communicative value.

Some dogs respond playfully when humans get into the play bow posture. One way to help anxious children take some risks while directing their attention outside themselves is to use this posture. The therapist gets into a play bow and helps the child do the same. The dog is then introduced, and a game is played with the dog when the dog responds to the play invitation. This process can be challenging for some children who fear looking foolish, and the therapist must use his or her knowledge of the child and good judgment when deciding to use this intervention. If done playfully, with the therapist serving as a model, however, it usually can be used with most children.

Similar to this, the therapist can teach the child to do the "dog shake" (Rohnke, 1991). The therapist demonstrates how the shake starts at the head, moves to the shoulders and arms, moves down through the trunk and hands, and then down the legs to the feet. The therapist and child practice this together in a playful fashion. Because of the muscle involvement and laughter that ensues, it usually has a physical and emotional relaxation effect.

A very easy method is to involve children in howling games. Pretending to howl like a dog can release tensions through the laughter it usually brings. This can be made much more enjoyable by doing it with a real dog who is likely to howl when it hears humans making howling sounds.

Some children experience sensory problems, including tactile defensiveness. They become anxious when clothing labels rub their skin or when their hands are dirty. While some of these children, especially those with sensory integration problems, can benefit from occupational therapy, the use of canine playfulness can also be applied to ease their anxieties. Although therapy dogs are kept clean and well groomed, they still have some messy characteristics, such as drool or shedding. With due consideration of the child's tolerance of anxiety, the therapist can introduce canine-related activities that refocus the child's attention to the dog's play while managing some slightly messy things.

> An example of this is an activity I have dubbed "Slobber Ball," in which the child simply plays ball with the dog. The ball invariably is covered with saliva when the dog returns it to the child. If the child squirms or comments about how "yucky" it feels, I simply suggest they quickly wipe their hands on a small towel I provide and get back to the game. Because the dog is eagerly waiting for the next throw, there is little time for the child to focus on the anxiety that comes with dirty hands. I take the child's anxiety seriously, but I handle it in a light-hearted or nonchalant tone: "That IS yucky, isn't it?? I don't like it either, but that's why we call it Slobber Ball. Here's a towel to wipe your hands. Look – Kirrie is waiting for the next throw." Most children are motivated to play with the dog to a degree that exceeds their anxiety, and I frequently see children who are sensitive to tactile discomfort initiate the ball game in subsequent sessions, often without my prompting or the use of a towel.

The types of playful interactions outlined in this section can reduce anxiety and help children release the feelings of joy and freedom that often are associated with playfulness. The use of play therapy dogs can help shift self-conscious children's focus from themselves to the dog, provide opportunities for play-oriented risk-taking, and release the laughter and fun that have been repressed or suppressed. Dogs provide excellent models of playfulness, of living in the present, and of unself-conscious enjoyment of life. Children seem to respond well to the invitation to play that comes from a play therapy dog, sometimes much more readily than from a play therapist. Research on the generalizability of these reactions is needed, but many children seem eager to learn ways to feel more relaxed in their daily lives after experiencing it first-hand with the dog in play therapy. Based on things that children have said during play sessions, it seems that canine play therapy helps them reconnect to their playful selves and helps break the ice so that they are willing to try other anxiety reduction approaches in play therapy and at home.

The play therapist must know the play therapy dog extremely well in order to use its naturally occurring playfulness and funny behaviors in therapeutic ways. The therapist must also use empathy and solid clinical judgment to decide when to introduce various play activities, especially the ones in which the child might feel frightened, embarrassed, or too silly. With these considerations in mind, the therapist, with the help of a canine play therapist, can help children harness the power of play, which in turn can be employed to facilitate the therapeutic progress of the child.

GRIEF AND LOSS

You think dogs will not be in heaven? I tell you, they will be there long before any of us.
                                    -Robert Louis Stevenson

Children's lives are touched by grief and loss, just as adults' are. The rituals surrounding death are geared primarily to adults, however, and children can become confused or frightened if their grieving needs are not addressed. Canines in play therapy can play several roles to help children through these difficult times.

GRIEVING THE LOSS OF A
HUMAN FAMILY MEMBER

Play therapists employ many methods to assist children with grief, including drawings, storytelling, children's books about death, memory books, sandtrays, therapeutic funerals, and playful celebrations of what the person meant to the child. Children naturally respond to grief situations in their play, and nondirective play sessions are often filled with symbols of children's grief following a family death.

> After the 9/11 attacks, I trained a number of play therapists in New York City to work with children and families in a variety of settings. Filial Therapy was used with a number of families who lost loved ones. In the nondirective parent-child play sessions, children frequently played out themes related to the attacks, building tall structures that they smashed with planes, burying bodies in the sandtray, and war scenes in which the "bad guys" were crushed. Parents were sometimes concerned about the children's light mood as they played somewhat gruesome themes, and the therapists involved helped them understand that children needed the lightness, playfulness, and distance of these types of play sessions to feel safe enough to express their grief. They were grieving, but in ways typical of children.

Because of dogs' ability to respond to human emotion, they can sometimes serve as a comfort to children who are grieving the loss of a grandparent, parent, sibling, or friend. Similar to play therapy interventions, dogs can provide solace without the intensity that typifies adult grieving. Therapists can educate families about the value of playtime with the family pet, or the benefit of stroking a pet's fur while telling the animal about what has happened.

Play therapists also can suggest that children tell the canine play therapist about what is happening in their lives. Children can draw pictures of their loved one and show them to the dog. There are countless ways in which the dog can be included as a witness to the child's feelings. The mere presence of the dog in the playroom, where the child might choose to relax and pet the dog or cry on the dog's shoulder, can be beneficial to the grief process.

> When 8-year-old Kiki lost her grandmother, she was already in play therapy for school-related anxiety. She had been close to her

grandmother and knew that she would not be seeing her again. My dog at the time, a Keeshond named Meisje, was known for her sensitivity to human tears. In the nondirective play session that immediately followed her grandmother's funeral, Kiki played with the miniature caskets, burying them in the sand. Near the end of the session, she asked if she could play with Meisje. I invited Meisje into the playroom, and Kiki showed her the sandtray she had created. We then moved to another room with Meisje, and I suggested to Kiki, "Why don't you tell Meisje all about the sad thing that happened with your grandmother? And then maybe you could tell Meisje a couple stories about some of the cool memories you have of your grandma." Kiki eagerly told Meisje all about the funeral and then told her about a time when she and her grandma had gone to the zoo together. Kiki cried a little as she told her stories, and Meisje gently put her paw on Kiki's leg. Although this interaction did not need much facilitation, I did comment, "Meisje really seems to know just how sad you feel and how much you miss your very special grandma."

GRIEVING THE LOSS OF A COMPANION ANIMAL

Adults sometimes underestimate the importance of family pets to children. Children confide in them, play with them, sleep with them, and consider them friends. When a pet dies, children can experience profound grief, with many of the same feelings they would have for a family member. Play therapists can help children express their grief in an accepting environment.

The books *Dog Heaven* and *Cat Heaven* (Rylant, 1995, 1997) have comforted many children, and the lighter tone of the writing provides the safety needed for children to grieve. Parents have commented that these books were helpful with their own grief, as well. *Saying Goodbye to Lulu* (Demas & Hoyt, 2004) is another book that helps children understand illness and death in pet dogs. There are many animal-themed books that help children with grief, and The Self-Esteem Shop (www.selfesteemshop.com) is a useful resource for these and other titles.

Play therapists can also suggest some activities devoted to the memory of the pet. One involves holding a therapeutic funeral in the sandtray, where the child can bury a small miniature representing the pet, saying whatever message they wish, either aloud or silently. Creating a memory book all about the animal's life can incorporate happy memories, sad feelings, and messages about the pet. The therapist can suggest the child draw pictures, obtain actual pictures, and write stories that are then combined in a simple book. Desktop publishing software now makes it relatively easy and quick to create a book from the child's memories.

> When a beloved dog, Minnie, died in one family, I asked the three children, ages 3, 7, and 10, to each draw a picture of something about Minnie that made them smile – a happy memory. They all eagerly did so, and then each of them wrote a story about Minnie. The 10-year-old wrote her story herself, and the younger children dictated their stories to me. All of this work was then compiled into a "Memories of Minnie" book that was fastened with a binding comb on one end. A copy was made for each child. The older children took their books to school to show some of their friends.

GRIEVING THE LOSS OF A THERAPY DOG

Sometimes therapy animals grow old and "retire," become ill, or suddenly die. The children's direct relationship with these animals ends. Many of the grieving activities described previously can be used in this situation, as well. The *Dog Heaven* (Rylant, 1995) book has helped many children when their canine therapist has died. The human therapist is likely to have feelings of loss as well, which can be shared with children as a way of acknowledging the special relationship they all shared. Of course, the therapist should share only as much as is in the therapeutic best interests of the child and reserve other grieving for private times at home.

If the dog is ill, children usually ask about it, and the therapist can help them create a get-well card if they wish. If the dog is not likely to return for therapy work, the therapist can write a personalized letter to the child on behalf of the dog, using the dog's voice, such as "I'm sorry I can't see you because I am sick. I miss you. You are a very special boy/girl, and I am very lucky that we have been friends. I still smile when I think of the time you pretended I was your baby and you let me drink from the baby bottle. I will always be your friend and we will always remember each other, okay? Woof woof!" If the dog died suddenly, the therapist can deliver a similar message to the child on behalf of the dog, "Before he died, Tory told me to tell you that. . . ." Simple messages are best.

BUILDING COMPETENCE
AND CONFIDENCE

A dog teaches a boy fidelity, perseverance, and to turn around three times before lying down.
                                        -Robert Benchley

Although the turning around skill may not be that useful for children, there are many skills that play therapy canines can help children develop, and those competencies can have a positive impact on children's self-image and confidence. Building on children's strengths can be one of the most beneficial ways to help them reduce their defenses and resolve many social, emotional, and behavioral problems. Canines in play therapy can provide some very real opportunities for children to develop their competence and confidence.

In the play therapy context, children can learn to train dogs in obedience, agility, and tricks. Children learn a variety of skills while working with the dog, including relationship building, consistency, patience, assertiveness, kindness, sharing, giving positive feedback, and perseverance. When the play therapist helps them understand the "why"s of various training methods along with the "how to"s, children learn a great deal with possible applications to other parts of their lives.

HELPING CHILDREN LEARN
ABOUT CANINE "LANGUAGE"

A first step to building children's confidence with dogs is to teach them some of the dog's behavioral signals. Many materials are available for showing children signs of canine anxiety, playfulness, or potential danger (Dunbar, 1996a; Kalnajs, 2006b; Rugaas, 2006; www.doggonesafe.com; www.doggonecrazy.ca). Learning these aspects of canine language can build children's confidence by giving them tools with which they understand dogs better and interact with them more skillfully. They also develop an area of "expertise" that they can share with friends and family.

TEACHING CHILDREN HOW TO
OBEDIENCE TRAIN A DOG

Canines used in play therapy should already be trained and easily managed by the play therapist. Training is a never-ending task, however, as dogs easily drift away from the lessons they have learned if they are not repeated. In this intervention, the therapist teaches the child basic obedience cues and gestures, how to deliver them, how to use lure-rewards, how to follow through if the dog does not listen, how to mark desired behaviors with a clicker, and how to reinforce the dog with treats, praise, or play. One of the most effective models for teaching these behaviors to children involves three steps: description, modeling, and skill practice.

Description. The therapist first describes the canine behavior that is desired; what words to say; any hand signals that are used; how to use a clear, firm, nonpunitive tone of voice; what to do if the dog does not comply; and how to reinforce the dog with praise, an excited voice, and/or training treats if it does what is asked. Focus on just one or two canine behaviors at a time is recommended. The video by Dunbar (1996a) is a valuable tool for this process with children. Descriptions should be very brief.

Modeling. The therapist then shows the child how it is done. The dog is involved in this step, and the therapist simply demonstrates the verbal and nonverbal cues and follow through that have previously been described. It is useful to repeat this demonstration three or four times as the child watches because there are many things for a child to remember even when focusing on a single cue.

Skill Practice. Now the child practices the same process that was demonstrated. The therapist steps aside or behind the child and gives the child an opportunity to try it. Children are not likely to get it completely correct the first several times, and the therapist needs to be patient and encouraging. As the child practices, the therapist praises the aspects that the child is doing correctly and gives just one or two suggestions for improvement in the weaker areas. The therapist can provide commentary in a soft voice as the action is happening. The feedback to the child should focus overwhelmingly on the things the child is doing well.

For example, as one child practiced giving Kirrie the cue to "Look!" (look at the child's face) and "Come!" (to come to the child from a position across the room), I stood several feet away and softly said, "That's great, Billy. You remembered the words. You also pointed to your eye. Terrific." After a couple trials of this, I said, "You're really getting the hang of this, Billy. You're doing great. Now try to make your voice sound more excited when you say 'Come.' " When he used a more animated voice, I commented, "That's it. Now you sound excited. Look how Kirrie is really paying attention to you now. You are learning fast how to train dogs!"

This positive approach to skill development for children builds motivation and confidence while giving the child specific behavioral feedback that is likely to increase skill acquisition. It is based on the empowerment approach used by Drs. Bernard and Louise Guerney so successfully in Filial Therapy with parents (Guerney, 1983; VanFleet, 2005).

Canines can be a bit confused by the child's fledgling efforts that may sound quite different from the play therapist/handler's commands, and sometimes they do not always follow the child's cue. The therapist minimizes this by focusing on just one or two cues and giving the child specific feedback. If the situation continues to confuse the dog, however, the therapist might take a break and ask the child to practice with a dog puppet or stuffed animal toy before resuming practice with the actual dog.

It is not a problem if the dog does not follow through each time, and, in fact, it can be beneficial to the process. It shows the child that animals are not predictable and that sometimes things go wrong, but with patience and persistence, the child can help the dog get it right. (In many ways, this is a parallel process to the teaching method the therapist is using with the child!) A dog that fails to follow through on the cues sometimes actually adds to the "real-ness" of the situation.

With the therapist's help and encouragement, the child and dog gradually begin working together better, and the sense of accomplishment for the child is great. Children who successfully give cues to the dog almost always want to learn more, and many of them want to demonstrate what they have learned to their parents. Building on the child's strengths in this manner increases the child's motivation, not only in training the dog, but in other areas of therapy and life, as well.

The sense of competence and confidence is invaluable to therapeutic progress in general.

> Using this approach has never failed with any child or adolescent with whom I have used it. They universally become engaged and excited about the process, and their increasing motivation shows clearly. The dog's behavior provides clear evidence and reinforcement of the child's efforts. A 16-year-old girl, Marnie, who had been truant from school and had a history of physical fights with other girls came to therapy reluctantly. She told me that the problems were with all the others, and that she did not have any problems. We talked about my approach and I initially used some cognitive-behavioral and expressive play therapy interventions with her. She was cooperative but remained quite guarded. Marnie liked Kirrie and told me that dogs could be trusted, unlike people. Although she tried, she could not hide her excitement at training and playing with the dog. As she practiced the cues with Kirrie, and the dog came running to her every time, I could see the corners of her mouth wiggling, as if she were trying to hold back her smiles. Before long, she was smiling broadly and enthusiastically praising Kirrie for listening to her. When we shifted from training to playing ball with Kirrie, she turned to me with a large smile and said, "Can we do this every time?" Marnie had become accustomed to feeling like a failure, and this simple success enlivened her.

The dog training sessions should be kept short – just 5 or 10 minutes – and they can be followed by a short child-canine playtime. The therapist teaches children the same cues and methods that are used on a regular basis at home with the dog. To reinforce the hands-on practice, the therapist might provide the child with a booklet detailing cues the dog knows. A sample, "Kirrie's Doggie Dictionary," is available online at www.playfulpooch.org.

PLAYING BALL

Playing ball or other "fetch" games can help children's developing relationship with the dog, and the dog's reaction is usually very reinforcing for them. Seeing a dog bounding happily back to play with them again and again helps children feel special and accepted. Children gain confidence from these interactions. Of course, playing ball or fetch is possible only with dogs who engage in those behaviors.

For dogs who enjoy chasing and returning objects such as balls, the therapist or dog handler should initially teach the dog how to release the object once it is returned. Verbal cues of "Drop It" or "Release" are often used, after which the dog drops the ball from its mouth. The child must learn the appropriate cue, as well. This process prevents possible injury from a child trying to grab the object from the dog's mouth.

> Kirrie is a tireless ball player. When I was first teaching her to release the ball, I was unable to bend over due to a temporary back injury. I taught her to release the ball into my open, slightly cupped hand when I said, "Hand!" I teach this command to children, instructing them to leave their hand open, or to cup both hands together with little curvature of the fingers – just enough to keep the ball from rolling out. The dog then drops the ball into the small pocket formed by their hands. They never need to reach for the ball or take it from the dog. This type of handoff also makes it easy to play ball with her while wearing gloves or mittens in the winter. This procedure not only adds safety, but children enjoy giving her the command and seeing her immediately drop the ball wherever they have placed their hands. One child who was an avid Little League baseball player pretended he was the catcher, using his hands as if they were a catcher's mitt.

AGILITY TRAINING

The use of agility training with children is discussed in more detail in the section on weight reduction, but it can also be used to build the child's competence and confidence. The same instructional approach of description, modeling, and skill practice with therapist reinforcement is valuable here, as well.

TEACHING THE CANINE NEW TRICKS

Children and adolescents enjoy watching a dog "perform" tricks, even simple ones such as sitting up or shaking hands. Another canine play therapy approach that builds children's skills and self-efficacy is to show them how to teach funny tricks to the dog. This often works best after the child has learned some basic obedience training and knows how to give simple cues and reinforcements. Here, the therapist and child decide a new trick for the dog to learn, taking into account the dog's personality, natural interests, and ability to learn. Together they work over several sessions using behavioral shaping to teach the trick. This takes approximately 10 minutes each time, and the therapist and child can discuss progress or obstacles to the dog's training afterward. There are many good resources that give instructions on how to teach new tricks to a dog (Bielakiewicz, 2005; Hodgson, 2001; Langbehn, 2003; Ludwig, 1996; Ray & Harding, 2005; Rock, 1998; Rosenthal, 1999).

The therapist must be attuned to the canine's limits when teaching new tricks in a therapeutic setting. While dogs can learn many new things throughout their lifetimes, it could be stressful for a dog to learn several new tricks at the same time from several different children. The therapeutic value of teaching new tricks must be balanced with considerations of the dog's welfare. If this process is not enjoyable and successful for the dog as well, then the canine's motivation is lost. Having several therapy dogs available can alleviate the pressures on a single animal to meet the needs of many children, or carefully limiting the amount of child-training that the dog is exposed to during the week is critical. Once a therapist sees the effectiveness of dog training for building children's strengths, it can be tempting to use it more often than the dog can tolerate. The therapist must monitor signs of canine stress and fatigue, both during sessions and in a more general way via the dog's behavior and energy levels at home.

> As an adolescent, I spent much time with our family dog, and I clearly remember the 2 days that I spent teaching her how to hold a cheese curl snack between her teeth and "Hold It!" until I said "Okay," whereupon she could eat it. I never made her hold it for more than a few seconds, and once she learned this trick, she never forgot it. What I remember most clearly, however, is how much patience it took with the many repetitions, how I could see small signs of progress that kept me at it (the cheese snacks were enough to keep the dog interested), and the tremendous pride that I felt when she "got it" and I was able to snap a picture of her holding the tidbit. I also remember how the dog responded so eagerly to the positive approach I used. Although I was not beyond yelling at the dog when frustrated, I learned something important about positive approaches during those 2 days, long before I ever heard of operant conditioning, continuous reinforcement schedules, shaping, chaining, and the like. Whenever I help children teach dogs new tricks, I see the same pride in their accomplishments as I felt.

In a therapy setting, the therapist ensures that only positive methods are used with the child and the dog, that complex canine behaviors are taught by shaping the responses, and that the dog is not teased at any time. The therapist needs to keep the atmosphere light, without any pressure for performance on either the child or the canine.

WEIGHT REDUCTION AND FITNESS

Now that we have Spunky, I go out and play with him a lot. I don't just watch TV and eat snacks like before.
-Jason, a 16-year-old boy

Although some children and families are referred to mental health professionals specifically for weight reduction, many children with eating disorders or weight problems enter therapy for different reasons, such as anxiety, depression, behavior problems, power struggles at home, medical problems, social difficulties, school problems, and trauma. Besides being a health risk that can lead to lifelong weight struggles, childhood obesity is also linked with social ostracism, victimization, and poor psychosocial adjustment (Latner & Schwartz, 2005; Robinson, 2006).

Treatment for overweight and obese children and adolescents is generally multimodal, and it must address the root causes of the problems that are determined on an individual basis. Canine play therapy can serve as an adjunct treatment, however. Most notably, it can provide an atmosphere of acceptance and belonging, pleasurable life experiences, stress release, and motivation for exercise. Canine play therapy, in conjunction with nondirective and directive play therapy, behavior management, nutrition and medical interventions, family therapy, Filial Therapy, and others, can augment and facilitate the other work being done.

WALKING THE DOG

Children's weight problems are often related to parental and family factors (Davison & Birch, 2001; Golan & Weizman, 2001) and sometimes develop in the context of a genetic history coupled with a sedentary family lifestyle. When these families have dogs, it is not unusual to find an overweight dog along with other overweight family members. Although overweight parents might find it difficult to embrace exercise programs, children seem more willing to do so with the right encouragement, and overweight dogs are typically very responsive to more frequent exercise. They seem to enjoy being out and about, sniffing new places.

A simple intervention that entails the child walking the dog on a regular basis can provide increasing motivation for other physical activities. Neighborhood safety issues must be considered first, however. If the physical environment for walking the dog is deemed safe, or if a parent can accompany the child on the walks, then very simple preparations can help this occur. The therapist should also ask the parents about the dog's prior training, how well it walks on a lead, if there are any canine behavioral problems, and if there are any areas the child should avoid, such as yards with barking dogs that could agitate the family pet. Of course, families walking dogs together are most likely to maintain the process and experience success.

The therapist asks the child to bring in photographs of the family pet and, on some occasions, can ask the child to actually bring the dog. Then the therapist excitedly tells the child how dogs enjoy seeing and sniffing the world and that they are happier and live longer when they go on frequent walks. The therapist shows the child and family the best ways to walk a dog, how to talk with the dog as they stroll, how to start with short distances and gradually increase, how to manage difficult canine behaviors, and so on. The child and family might also need some basic training on how to walk a dog on a lead, how to hold the lead, what to do if the dog pulls, and so on (see Dunbar, 1996a). The key is to help the family structure the environment so that the child is likely to succeed.

When the child returns after being sent out on the mission to walk the dog, the therapist inquires about the things the child and dog saw or experienced on their walk, what things the dog was most interested in, and so on. This follow-up is important to maintaining motivation. If the child or family did not follow through on the plan, the therapist can troubleshoot to determine possible obstacles and ways to overcome them. Throughout this process, the focus is on the dog rather than the child, and the atmosphere is playful and light.

> Jenny was 11 years old and obese. She and her family were
> involved in a weight reduction and family therapy program at a local

hospital, and she had been referred to me by that program to work on self-esteem and resistance issues. She was quiet and depressed, and she indicated very few interests except for favorite television programs. Others had tried to interest her in hobbies and activities without success. At home, Jenny lived with her obese mother and overweight father, and the family typically gathered around the television at night. They also had a Beagle mix dog, who the veterinarian had told them was overweight.

Because I also lived with Beagles who had a tendency to eat too much, Jenny responded positively to discussions about our dogs and how hard it was to keep them trim. I then told her a story about how my Beagles just loved to sniff things and how excited they got when I walked them. At my invitation, she brought her Beagle to the next session, and I brought one of mine. We walked our dogs together in a private area outdoors. I pointed out how fascinated the Beagles were with every little detail and how it was sometimes difficult to walk with them because their noses were always leading them astray. We laughed together and talked about what life must be like to have such a sensitive nose. At the end of that session, we developed a dog-walking plan for her, and I supplemented that on subsequent meetings with eight nondirective play sessions. At the time, I thought Filial Therapy might benefit the family, but I did not offer it because they were already involved in family therapy.

Our referral source at the weight reduction program reported that Jenny became much more interested in the exercise portions of her plan after 3 weeks of dog walking. Jenny had even asked the medical staff if her dog could take part in the exercises they were recommending for her. Jenny made steady weight loss progress from that point on. The credit for her weight loss resides solidly with her weight reduction and family therapy program and her own efforts, but the dog walking and play therapy interventions can be attributed with the resolution of her resistance and increase of her motivation to participate.

CANINE AGILITY TRAINING

Dog agility is defined by the United States Dog Agility Association as "a competitive sport that tests a person's skills in training and handling of dogs over a timed obstacle course. Competitors race against the clock as they direct their dogs to jump hurdles, scale ramps, burst through tunnels, traverse a see-saw, and weave through a line of poles in an obstacle course configuration designed to challenge a handler's competitive and training skills. With scoring based on faults similar to equestrian show jumping, dog agility has become an exciting spectator event" (www.usdaa.com). Participants in canine agility typically describe it as "fun" and a "great way to stay in shape."

Canine agility can be used several ways with children, and it has potential for weight reduction as well as for building confidence and self-esteem. First, children with their own pet dogs can become junior agility handlers and participate competitively. Second, children can engage in agility with their dogs simply for fun, without competing. Third, children can set up their own agility course in the back yard, with makeshift hurdles and obstacles that they then run through with their dog. Fourth, therapists who have done agility training with their own dogs can set up a course near their work and invite children to join them to learn the basics. Fifth, children can participate alongside human-canine agility teams in a variety of community events, such as the On Course for Kids program for child cancer patients mentioned earlier in this monograph (www.dogsofcourse.com).

The United States Dog Agility Association (www.usdaa.com), the North American Dog Agility Council (www.nadac.com), the American Kennel Club (www.akc.org), and the United Kennel Club (www.ukcdogs.com) all have more information on this sport, including junior handler programs, and there are local clubs where families can attend events and learn how to become more involved. Therapists who recommend this possible intervention should discuss potential ramifications of competitive activity with the child and family. Once again, the key is to create an environment in which children enjoy themselves with their pets and feel successful. If the competitive nature of agility trials is likely to increase stress, then the modified, noncompetitive forms of the sport are probably more likely to be sustained by the child.

FITNESS

Many children today, even though within healthy weight parameters, are considerably less active physically. The popularity of television and computer games has contributed to more sedentary and isolated lifestyles. The canine-related activities mentioned for weight reduction can easily be used to promote fitness and physical well-being, too. One excellent private website by Diane Blackman, www.dogplay.com, lists over 40 playful and active things that people can do with their dogs. Links are provided to obtain more information on all of them.

ATTACHMENT AND RELATIONSHIP BUILDING: CANINE APPLICATIONS FOR MALTREATED AND TRAUMATIZED CHILDREN

Histories are more full of examples of the fidelity of dogs than of friends.
                                        -Alexander Pope

The mental health of children and adults depends largely upon the nature of their relationships. Secure human attachments have been shown to be critical for emotional and social development (Belsky & Nezworski, 1988; Clark & G. W. Ladd, 2000; James, 1994; G. W. Ladd & B. K. Ladd, 1998). Children who have experienced anxious attachments, trauma, and/or disruptions to the attachment process, such as maltreatment, domestic violence, exposure to substance abuse in the family, or numerous placements within the foster care system, often develop emotional and behavioral problems that can become quite serious and difficult to treat (James, 1994; Terr, 1990; VanFleet & Sniscak, 2003). Facilitating healthy attachment experiences has become an important feature of treatment.

The strength and importance of the human-animal bond has been outlined previously in this monograph, and this section looks at ways canines in play therapy can develop, strengthen, and sustain healthy attachments for children who have suffered trauma, maltreatment, and disruptions in their attachment processes. These children sometimes seem to develop attachments to dogs more readily than to humans. To what extent canine attachments can then be generalized to human relationships remains an important potential area for empirical study, but hundreds of personal accounts and case studies suggest that this does indeed occur.

Sandi was a 15-year-old girl who had lived in foster care for 6 years. She had a history of neglect and physical and sexual abuse. She had lived in over 14 homes, usually being moved when foster parents were unable to manage her behavioral outbursts. She had a history of hurting animals, and many changes in placement were precipitated when she tried to injure family pets. Eventually she was placed with the Reed family, which had two dogs. Karen Reed supervised all of Sandi's interactions with the dogs and taught her how to treat them. Sandi later told her therapist, "I'd reached the point where I just didn't trust *any* grown-ups. They hurt me over and over. But those dogs seemed to love me just for being me, and I loved them, too. I think that was the first time I ever felt loved. I told them all about my problems. I know they didn't really understand me, but it just felt good to be able to talk to them. After a while, I realized that Karen was okay. She's the one who showed me how to be nice to the dogs, and I figured that if the dogs liked her, maybe she was okay after all. I began to trust her more and more. Now I can talk with her about almost anything. She's like the mom I never really had."

The remainder of this section explores ways that canines can be integrated into play therapy interventions that are designed to facilitate attachment and to repair some of the damage that has occurred from prior traumatic experiences.

THIS DOG IS JUST LIKE ME!

When parents, teachers, therapists, or other adults focus directly on children's behaviors or problems, children can feel self-conscious and defensive. Helping children focus on problem areas in less direct ways can yield improvements more readily. Because canines often have behavior problems or challenges similar to children's, therapists can use perceived similarities to help the child connect with the dog and at the same time focus on problem areas.

Josh was 13 years old, and had spent nearly 5 years in foster care. He had a history of serious physical abuse that left him traumatized and untrusting of adults. His trauma and attachment history often erupted in behavior problems, and he had been moved through several foster homes and possible adoptive placements. He had teased dogs and cats in some of these placements, and he had caused some minor injuries to family pets. His background sounds much like Sandi's because these situations are common among foster children.

Before he met or worked with Kirrie, I described her history to him, emphasizing aspects to which he could relate from his own history. I spoke about how Kirrie had not been treated in the loving manner that she deserved, and that for reasons I just could not understand, she had not been wanted by her first family. I likened her stay at the dog shelter and then at the Border Collie rescue to "doggie foster care." I then explained how we had adopted her, how wonderful and special she was, and that she did have some problems that we were working on as she adjusted to living with us and learning to trust us. Josh, who usually had a short attention span, listened intently while I explained her history, nodding his head as "one who knows" and asking a few questions.

This background helped Josh see the similarities between himself and Kirrie, and it set the stage for later interventions when I asked him to help me resolve some of her difficulties.

It is important that this information be based on the truth about the dog, as the therapist knows it. Different emphases can be used to match the dog's characteristics in an individualized way to some of the child's characteristics, and small embellishments of the story are fine. Nevertheless, the therapist should avoid exaggerating the problems too far from actual behaviors. Client children do not need to see the dog as a duplicate of themselves. A few points in common are sufficient for the children to be able to relate to the canine's history, problems, and progress.

In a more general way, therapists can use children's books featuring animals to establish common experiences and hope. For example, *Sheep* (Hobbs, 2006) details the transitions of one dog's many homes and names, and its travels in search of its purpose in life. Jack, as he is eventually called, finds a young boy in a residential facility awaiting adoption. The story details the dog's history of good and bad experiences that eventually triumph in a secure home.

ACCEPTANCE: CANINE-STYLE

I am I because my little dog knows me.
-Gertrude Stein

Children who have suffered maltreatment rarely have felt accepted and understood by adults. Often, their relationships have been unhealthy reversals to normal attachment processes, with the child expected to meet adult needs in completely unrealistic ways and with dire consequences for failure to do so. By the time they are involved with kinship or foster care, they have learned to distrust adults completely. They frequently feel misunderstood and ostracized by peers, as well.

Acceptance of the child's *self* is critical for the development of a strong identity, secure attachment, healing, and overall psychosocial health. Nondirective play therapy and Filial Therapy focus heavily on acceptance of the child's feelings, reactions, and wishes, and these modalities are often used early in the treatment of maltreated children to establish trust as well as throughout therapy to help overcome the negative consequences of maltreatment. Even so, therapists, as well as foster, kinship, and adoptive parents, no matter how accepting and kind, are still adults to be viewed with suspicion. The child might well be thinking, "Even though these adults treat me well, can I really trust them? People always seem to betray and hurt me. I'd better play it safe and keep my defenses up so I don't get hurt again."

Canines, on the other hand, do not often trigger this caution in these children. In fact, dogs seem to invite the child's trust in ways that no human can. Children seem to feel the dog's acceptance immediately, and it seems irresistible. Children open up with dogs when they cannot safely do so with humans. Having a canine play therapist helps children feel accepted in nearly every interaction. The dog greets them with recognition, friendly tail-wagging, and licking. The dog's affectionate behavior is unwavering, and children know that the dog will be happy to see them, even if they have had a bad day in school or at home. As one adolescent put it, "Meisje [dog] doesn't care if I got suspended in school today. She likes me even when I get in trouble."

Canine acceptance is perhaps one of the most noted traits that endear dogs to people. Quotations from authors, poets, researchers, and philosophers through the ages frequently mention the dog's loyalty and steadfastness. Play therapists can harness this quality any time that they employ the services of a therapy dog. Using a trained canine in nondirective play sessions provides children with empathy from both the human and canine therapists, opening more doors for healing. Allowing the canine and child to play together in other play therapy interventions strengthens bonds that can serve as a frame of reference for healthier human relationships to come.

Josh often engaged in imaginary role play during nondirective play sessions. He cast himself in the role of a police officer who was trying to capture the "bad guys," often portrayed by some large dolls. He told me I was his wife, also a police officer, who stayed home to take care of our babies. Battles would ensue, and Josh's character was injured, often by being shot or knocked out. He hinted that I was to help him when this happened, and I did so by using the doctor's kit to check him out, give him medicine, and patch up his wounds. This type of play happened several times before Josh met Kirrie.

Kirrie was added to play sessions with Josh, and we used her for directive and nondirective play sessions. When Kirrie was in the nondirective play sessions, Josh placed her in the role of family watchdog. She was there to keep his family safe. When the dog wanted to engage with Josh's imaginary police play, I told her to stay, saying, "Kirrie, Stay. You must stay here. Your dad will tell us if he needs you." When he fell to the floor, Kirrie rushed to his side with me (as Josh had instructed me). As I doctored him, Kirrie licked his neck and cheek. I kept checking him and giving him medicine as we had played before, incorporating Kirrie into some of my statements: "Kirrie, your father's down! We have to help him. I'm checking him out. I think he needs medicine – fast! Oh, Kirrie, you're licking him. You're worried about him, too. You're giving him the 'Lick of Life.'" Josh would lie still for a time while we fussed over him, but he eventually got back up and finished off the bad guys. At times, he enlisted Kirrie's help in fighting the bad guys, holding them near her mouth while I pretended she was chewing them up. All of this imaginary play was enacted as Josh wanted and in accordance with the roles that he had assigned to all of us.

Josh was very pleased that Kirrie could join our nondirective play sessions, and he seemed to benefit from her acceptance of him in all of the activities that we did together. When he left our geographic region for nearly a year for another foster placement, Kirrie "wrote" him a number of therapeutic letters (discussed later in this section), and when he returned to treatment after his adoption by a family back in our area, his first question to me was, "I wonder if Kirrie will remember me." He was thrilled when she obviously did.

SAFE BOUNDARIES

Children who have been maltreated usually have boundary confusion in terms of their physical selves, their safety, and in their relationships. Involving a canine in their play therapy sessions can help. First, the therapist shows the child how to play and interact safely with the dog. The therapist makes it clear that the child must keep safe and that the dog must be safe. Specific suggestions for doing so in any activity are made. The therapist then helps the child set appropriate boundaries as needed.

Josh was the first child to work with Kirrie, and although I had been trying to eliminate her jumping up behaviors, they were not entirely gone at that time. I taught Josh the "Off" command. I noticed that when she jumped on him, he gave the command in a high-pitched, melodic voice. I modeled how to use a "deep voice" when saying "Off." With reminders from me whenever Kirrie jumped up, Josh greatly improved his ability to give the command in a firm, deeper tone of voice. In essence, he learned how to keep himself safe. We coupled the command with other behaviors, such as standing up and turning his back on Kirrie if she did not immediately get off him.

Although I knew prior to this that maltreated and attachment-disrupted children often hurt animals, most likely because the animals are more vulnerable and the children can feel more powerful in repeating the abusive relationships with which they have been victimized, this experience led me to surmise that another factor may be involved, as well. Josh did not know how to keep himself safe with the dog. I saw how easily children could lash out at a dog who accidentally stepped on them or bumped them when they did not know how to manage the animal's behavior or how to protect themselves. In just two sessions where Josh and I focused on using his deeper voice and using effective body postures to keep Kirrie on the floor, Josh was noticeably more confident, relaxed, and appropriate with Kirrie. He had been empowered to keep himself safe without hurting the dog. His foster mother at the time also reported immediate changes at home in his interactions with the family dog. He no longer hit the dog or yelled at it. He used the methods we had covered with Kirrie.

Dog "kisses" have provided a similar avenue to help children establish boundaries safely. Many children enjoy Kirrie's licks, but they learn the "Enough!" command to stop her whenever they no longer want her to lick them. Alternatively, Kirrie has learned to touch her nose on an outstretched open hand (targeting) to the verbal cue, "Kiss me." Some children prefer this to her licking and learn to establish their boundaries by using this alternative behavior.

FIRST THINGS FIRST: "LOOK!"

If the dog will not come to you after having looked you in the face, you should go home and examine your conscience.
            -Woodrow Wilson

Because dogs communicate a great deal through their eyes, as people do, a useful cue to teach a dog is "Look!" The dog makes eye contact, after which other commands can be given. It is a valuable cue for children to learn to use with a canine play therapist, and this can be done in the context of the "Look! Game." The therapist shows them how to say "Look!" in an excited manner and then move a training treat held in their fingers up to the corner of their eye. A dog who has been previously trained to follow this cue quickly makes eye contact with the child. The child then gives other obedience or play cues, such as "Get the ball!"

This simple procedure helps children learn, through the dog, to focus first before trying something more complex. It also appears to offer a more relaxed way to help children learn the importance of eye contact in their relationships.

Adults sometimes try to encourage eye contact from children in a sterile, textbook fashion. Sometimes it is associated with punishment: "Look at me when I'm talking to you!" This type of emphasis on eye contact is rarely successful and sometimes increases children's avoidance of eye contact. Eye contact is an important part of a relationship, but if the relationship does not feel safe, attempts to focus on this single behavior seem misguided. The use of a canine play therapist in the context of the "Look! Game" provides safety as well as reinforcement of children's use of their eyes in the context of a safe relationship.

> Many maltreated and attachment-disrupted children with whom I have worked seem to avoid eye contact when I first meet them. They seem to lack confidence and may actually be afraid to meet people's eyes. When we are engaged in play therapy, their wariness seems to fade, and they make more eye contact, especially when we engage in play activities together. I have noticed a similar reaction when using canines in play therapy. As children learn the "Look! Game," they also seem to make more eye contact with me. They look to me to get feedback on how they are doing. I usually do not say anything about their eye contact, and I simply meet their eyes, smile, and tell them how quickly they are learning to create a relationship with Kirrie. Sometimes I briefly talk about how Kirrie listens to them better and respects them because they can use their eyes when working with her.
>
> When I first trained Kirrie to respond to the "Look!" cue, I learned something unexpected. Initially I was very consistent, asking her to

look at me before all commands and also when we played fetch before each throw of the ball. She learned quickly and made eye contact consistently. After that, I rarely had to give the cue. As we played ball, I began to realize that she was looking at my eyes every time, yet as I daydreamed or thought about other things when tossing the ball, I rarely made eye contact with her. I became much more aware of my own inconsistencies in training and working with her, and it helped me improve my dog interaction skills and the way I model them for children.

HELPING TO TRAIN THE DOG

The use of basic canine obedience training with children is covered earlier in this monograph. It is a beneficial tool for working with children with abuse histories and attachment difficulties. Their confidence grows as they learn to protect themselves from harm. Learning canine signals and body language helps them learn to be more observant of others' behaviors and reactions (Kalnajs, 2006b; Rugaas, 2006). Bekoff's *Ranger Rick* article, "Play Fair" (2006) is a wonderful example of how children's awareness of canine behavior can be applied to their own. Learning to read signals in complex environments is an important part of human adaptation, just as it is with nonhuman animals. Learning to read and respond appropriately to a dog helps children develop skills that may assist not only with basic survival, but with the development of closer, healthier relationships, as well.

HEALTHY TOUCH: GROOMING, MASSAGE, AND CARING FOR A DOG

There are numerous ways that play therapists can use a dog to help children learn about physical well-being and caregiving. Parents often obtain pet dogs because they hope it will teach responsibility to their children. While this certainly can be the case, it often happens that children do not follow through with feeding, grooming, walking, and cleaning up after the novelty wears off. Parents become frustrated with their children, and the dog is viewed with annoyance or resentment. When a family has a pet, the therapist can assist parents in setting realistic expectations for their children and providing tips on ways to motivate their children to follow through with pet care.

In the therapy setting, as an adjunct to other play therapy work that involves the canine, children can learn better ways to care for their dogs. Even if they do not have a companion dog at home, learning to care for a dog can build attachment.

Maltreated children usually have had traumatic experiences with human touching. While touch is a vital part of human connection and attachment, they may fear touch and avoid it. On the other hand, they may have learned to touch in hurtful ways. In most cases, there is confusion about boundaries when it comes to physical closeness and contact.

With any or all of these purposes in mind, the therapist can use grooming and massage activities to help children. Children usually enjoy learning how to pet, touch, and groom a dog. The dog's enjoyment of this contact is a natural reinforcer for kind, gentle behaviors. The same is true of canine massage. Children can learn to pet a dog in calming ways or learn methods such as Tellington Touch (TTouch) or canine massage (Fox, 2004; Tellington-Jones, 1993, 2000, 2001, 2003). The therapist or dog handler learns these methods first and then teaches them to children to use for short periods. Again, the therapist's knowledge of the therapy dog's preferred "rubbing spots" helps the child handle the dog appropriately and in a manner that brings canine reinforcement for the child's care. Of course, the therapist praises the child's efforts.

> I know that each of my dogs has preferred ways to be touched. All of them calm down when their ears are stroked. Their ears are very soft, and children enjoy touching them. When someone massages the back of Jagen's neck, she gets a dreamy look in her eyes. Kirrie quickly rolls onto her back for belly rubs. Corky gently places a paw on people's forearms to invite a chest rub, and she pushes up on her hind legs in a comical manner when people pat or massage in front of her tail. I share this information with children during play sessions, and I help them use the correct amount of pressure by watching the dog's reactions to their touch. With children who seem unaware of how their touch might affect others, I place my hand under theirs while they are first touching the dog, and then I can give them feedback: "A little more. . . . A little lighter. That's just right."
>
> At times we end the canine play therapy portions of our sessions with brief "doggie massages." As children stroke the dogs as I have taught them, they seem to relax themselves, as well. It provides a comfortable transition for both the dog and the child.

Depending on the schedule, children also can help me feed the dogs, take them outside to do their "business," and take them for short walks in a private area of the property. Children's use of touch and caring is easily stimulated, and I praise them by pointing out how much the dog is connecting with them: "Corky really likes the way you are rubbing her chest. Stop for a minute and see what she does. See? She put her paw out to show you that she wants more. You are taking very good care of her and being very gentle."

EMPATHY "EXERCISES"

Dog owners and enthusiasts speak often of canines' empathy. Although there are different interpretations of this behavior in dogs, the factor of most importance for canine play therapy work is that children and adults *feel* as though the dogs are empathic. Canines do read human signals carefully and adjust their behavior accordingly, and this characteristic can be used to help children develop their own understanding of emotion in themselves and others. Many maltreated and attachment-disrupted children have never experienced empathy in their lives. Adult attempts to "teach" empathy for others to children before they have ever truly experienced it themselves seem misguided, although common. Children's own needs for acceptance and empathy must be satisfied first. It is much more likely that children will develop empathy *after* they have experienced it. The acceptance inherent in play therapy as well as in human-canine interactions can provide children with initial experiences of empathy.

Play therapists can build on these early empathy experiences with child-canine activities and games. "Fido's Feelings" is a general approach that encourages children to watch the dog's body language and expressions to identify how the dog might be feeling. Because canines' feelings are simple and straightforward, they provide a concrete way to introduce the complexities of human emotion and empathy to children who have little experience with them. A number of different activities can be called "Fido's Feelings" to create a playful climate. Therapists ask children to watch the therapy dog for signals that show how it is feeling, or they show photos or videos of dogs and ask children to identify the feelings. Dogs' emotions should not be made more complex than they are. Focus is on feelings of happiness or contentment, fear, aggression and protection, submission, excitement, and the like. With some brief instruction by the therapist followed by playful interactions with the play therapy dog, children are usually motivated to "read" the dog's signals and feelings.

> When Josh played ball with Kirrie, I cued him to watch for signs that she was getting tired. She ran slower, breathed harder, and sometimes walked back to us in comical slow-motion. With my help, Josh began to recognize these signs when they first appeared, and he would finish the ball game with several short, easy throws. After just a few play sessions, he watched for Kirrie's signals without prompting, and he spontaneously showed signs of empathy for the dog. One day he noticed a small spot of blood on her lip when he took the ball from her, saying to me, "Is she bleeding? Is she hurt?" I had not noticed the blood until he mentioned it, but we checked her out together and found a tiny injury from catching the ball against her lip.
>
> Prior to his involvement with Kirrie, Josh had shown concern for animals. He had found an injured wild bunny on his way to school and took it to the school nurse to be treated. He was suspended from school for his poor judgment. Although the school's concern with rabies or other threats to child safety was understandable, the decision unfortunately punished Josh for the one area in which he did show concern for others – with animals. With the therapy dog, he was able to express his concern and receive reinforcement for his empathy in a safe, controlled environment. I praised him for noticing and calling my attention to the injury. I also differentiated our roles. I was the one with the most dog handling experience who could safely check her mouth without being accidentally bitten. He had played the very important role of noticing the injury, informing an adult, and then helping to soothe Kirrie after I had checked her and all was safe.

It is unknown whether children's developed empathy for dogs transfers to humans, but one controlled study suggests that it can. A 40-hour animal-oriented humane education program given to elementary school students yielded greater empathy directed toward humans at the end of the program and 1 year later (Ascione, 1992; Ascione & Weber, 1996). Another study of adults abused as children showed that those who were able to experience healthy animal-human bonds were much less likely to abuse animals or their children than those who did not have such attachments (Nebbe, 1997). Reports from parents and foster parents also suggest that children who experience empathy and attachment with the therapist, play therapy dog, and parents in Filial Therapy seem to show more empathy for family members, but this assertion remains to be studied in a controlled way. These studies and reports suggest that the use of animals to create healthy, safe, and close relationships with distressed children has the potential to generalize to human and future relationships, and further study of this possibility is warranted because of its important implications for work with traumatized and attachment-disrupted children and families.

THE DOGGIE HOTLINE

Play therapists can also incorporate therapy dogs into cognitive-behavioral play therapy interventions designed to promote children's problem-solving skills. The *Doggie Hotline* is an adaptation of Kaduson's *News Network* (Kaduson, 2001, 2006) and *A Kid Like You* (Heidi Kaduson, personal communication, May 2, 2005) interventions. The therapist enlists the child's help in resolving canine problems while providing the child with coping strategies that can be applied to his or her own problems. For example, the therapist tells the child a story about the dog's problem behaviors and asks the child for advice about how to help the dog. At least some of the problems should be similar to those with which the child is grappling. The game can be played as part of a special televised "Animal Advice Show" in which pet owners call for suggestions from the guest expert, played by the child client. The therapist facilitates the activity by playing the show moderator as well as the callers. The interaction is videotaped. Another version involves sharing actual problems of the therapy dog with the child and asking for suggestions. Again, problems are raised that are similar to the child's, and the therapist guides the child to possible solutions, all the while staying in role. The play therapy dog may or may not be present for these interventions.

> I used this approach with Josh several times. In one of our early sessions, I asked Josh for his ideas to help Kirrie stop tearing up paper towels into tiny pieces all over the floor (an actual behavior of hers). When I asked him why she might be doing that, he replied, "She's probably nervous. Or maybe she had something bad happen to her once." As for suggestions, he thought more exercise and ball playing would help. He also suggested some petting to help her calm down. In a later session, we videotaped a Doggie Hotline Show in

which I asked his advice on another behavior problem similar to his. "My name is Mildred, and my dog Brutus keeps getting in trouble with other dogs. When he sees another dog, he growls and wants to fight, but I'm worried that someone will get hurt. What can I do to help Brutus when he feels angry or afraid and tries to fight?" With my prompting, Josh responded that I (Mildred) could help Brutus by helping him walk away or count to 10, and letting Brutus tear up an old phone book, all methods that others had suggested to Josh for his own anger control. Josh thoroughly enjoyed being the guest dog expert, and when we played this game yet again, he spontaneously dressed up as a police officer who was a K-9 expert appearing on the show.

SELF-PROTECTION AND SELF-REGULATION

Play may be viewed as a device for regulating the level of emotional arousal around sensitive, emotionally laden themes in the child's psyche.
                                        -Shlomo Ariel

Many of the canine play therapy interventions discussed in this section and elsewhere in this monograph contribute to children's overall sense of safety in the playroom and help with improved self-regulation. Children do not actively work through their difficulties until they feel emotionally safe. The play therapy process offers this safety, and the addition of a canine therapist appears to increase the child's sense of protection. Play seems to reduce the physiological arousal associated with trauma, anxiety, and other problems, and canines seem to enhance the play as well as add to the child's sense of safety.

Children must learn how to manage different levels of arousal, as do dogs. One way to assist this process is to permit the child to play an arousing game with the dog, placing the child in charge of the arousal level. The therapist shows the child how to play the game and then states that it is the child's job to keep himself or herself safe and to keep the dog safe. During the game, the therapist reinforces the child for managing the arousal level and offers brief reminders if the child has difficulty doing so.

There are many games that can be incorporated here. A safe use of rope toys or tug toys provides a competitive environment. Small tug toys or short rope toys should never be used, as they have higher potential for accidental injury. As the dog tries to bite the toy, it can inadvertently nip the child. (No biting games whatsoever should ever be used with a dog who has aggressive tendencies or a hard bite, and it is unlikely that such dogs would be good therapy dogs.) The use of a long rope toy (a distance of 2 feet or more between child and dog) and a dog with a soft bite (which often can be trained; see Donaldson, 2005), however, can be safely supervised by the therapist or dog handler. The therapist helps the child determine the safety rules and how to respond if the game becomes too rough or unsafe. Children do best when given concrete signs of hyperarousal in the dog or the game, such as the dog jumps up, knocks things over, gets within 2 feet of the child during the game, or races around the room. The therapist shows the child how to stop the game immediately by dropping the toy on the ground, standing up, saying "No!" firmly, and turning his or her back to the dog, thereby removing attention and reinforcement of the highly aroused behavior. The therapist provides quick, helpful reminders if the child does not set limits when needed.

In this type of mildly competitive game, the therapist also cues the child to permit the canine to "win" some of the time. Children learn that the dog does not enjoy the game unless it feels successful at times, and this also helps children manage their own arousal levels. Mutual satisfaction is important in play and in relationships, both with canines and humans. Finally, the therapist informs the family of the nature of this intervention and provides necessary cautions about using it at home with their own pets.

> Josh and Kirrie both seemed to enjoy the stimulation of the tug game they played with the long rope toy. Josh made growling noises and experimented with different ways of tugging on the rope that caused Kirrie to shake the rope vigorously in an attempt to wrest it from him. While Josh needed my reminders to slow the game down when it became too fast or expansive, he quickly learned to monitor the arousal levels and make adjustments independently. When Kirrie bounced up and down close to him, he stopped the game. If she continued her excited behaviors, he stood up and took a break. Josh did not mind letting Kirrie "win" in order to keep her interested in the game. After a few minutes playing this way, we switched to more calming activities for both Josh and Kirrie. His foster mother reported that he immediately began playing more appropriately with the family dog. He stopped roughhousing with the dog in a way that previously had led to scratches for Josh and angry reprisals on the dog. Nearly

2 years of problematic interactions with the family dog were reversed for the duration of his stay in that home through the therapeutic use of obedience training, self-protection measures, and proper management of arousal levels. This change in Josh's ability to self-regulate and manage his interactions with dogs continued through two additional foster placements and into his eventual adoptive home, spanning nearly a 3-year period.

Some canine or mental health professionals might disagree with *any* use of tugging games, and readers are urged to consider the potential risks before doing so. Donaldson's (2005) and Dunbar's (1996b) discussions of bite inhibition are very useful in this regard. If the risks can be managed well, there seem to be clinical benefits when children play livelier games with canines, learning to manage their own arousal and safety more effectively. Other game choices can accomplish similar outcomes.

TRANSITIONS: CANINE THERAPEUTIC
LETTER WRITING AND STORYTELLING

> *The one absolutely unselfish friend that man can have in this selfish world, the one that never deserts him, the one that never proves ungrateful or treacherous, is his dog.*
> -George G. Vest

Transitions can be difficult for children, especially those whose lives have been filled with frequent, unpredictable changes. Therapeutic storytelling and letter writing can incorporate canines quite easily. Telling stories about the therapy dog, a family pet, or an imaginary animal can provide metaphors for the child's struggles and resilience.

Many children's therapeutic books feature animals, most likely because children relate well to animal characters, animals provide some distance and emotional safety, and children more readily understand the message of the book (see www.selfesteemshop.com for many examples). A variety of storytelling approaches can be used to help children create their own stories about animals (e.g., Gallo-Lopez, 2001; VanFleet, 1993). Often, the stories children create about animals clearly reflect their own dilemmas, coping, and wishes.

The therapist can also use therapeutic letter writing, on behalf of the play therapy dog, to assist children with difficult situations or transitions. The therapist writes a letter from the dog to the child containing a message that might help the child. (Kirrie has also written a letter to professionals who use therapy dogs, and it is included in Appendix B, pp. 125-126, to provide an example of this approach.)

At a critical time in his treatment, Josh, then 14 years old, was placed with a foster family who lived too far away to bring him to our practice. The agency responsible for Josh indicated that he was likely to return to our area and to treatment with us but that he would be in this placement for 6 months or more. It turned out to be a year.

Because of Josh's history of neglect, abuse, and abandonment, the decision to move him threatened the many gains he had made in treatment. He had never done well with transitions, exhibiting very aggressive behaviors and emotional outbursts when moving from one home to another. The current move could not be helped, and it was unfortunate that the only available place for him also meant he could not continue therapy. I wanted to assure some sense of continuity for him, and I did so in two ways. First, I researched his new geographic region and found a competent therapist who was experienced with the trauma and attachment issues he had. Josh knew that I was looking for another therapist for him to see, and he seemed to appreciate that level of involvement. Second, I told him that Kirrie and I would stay in touch with him because we would be happy to work with him again when he returned to our area. During the time he was away, "Kirrie" sent him brief letters on a biweekly to monthly basis. She told stories of her own struggles with changes, feelings, and behaviors, and gave him some of her own tips that might be useful to him. I occasionally inserted a note from myself with encouraging words.

The new therapist who worked with Josh and his new foster parents told me that the letters were invaluable for Josh. This appeared to be his smoothest transition, and although problems did occur, they were less intense. While the reasons for his improved adjustment are not entirely known, Josh himself told me that he wanted the letters from Kirrie to continue, even when he was adopted. He eventually returned to our area and resumed therapy with his adoptive family. His adoptive parents reported that the "Kirrie Letters" remained very important to him and helped him with his reading skills. Filial Therapy was the primary intervention used to create strong, healthy attachments within the adoptive family, but Kirrie did work with him for short periods at the end of some of his filial play sessions.

In summary, many canine-child interactions can help children build stronger, healthier relationships. The features of human-canine attachment are not appreciably different from those of human-human attachments. For children with attachment difficulties, developing a healthy, reciprocal relationship with a dog might involve less emotional risk than more complex and demanding human relationships. After a child establishes a healthy relationship with a dog, a skillful therapist can use it as a template, or frame of reference, for the child's human relationships. It requires clinical skill to help children generalize and apply what they have learned, but it seems easier to build future relationships when children have had at least one good experience to draw from.

ATTENTIONAL AND BEHAVIORAL DIFFICULTIES

The worst loneliness is not to be comfortable with yourself.
-Mark Twain

Canines can augment play therapy for children with attention-deficit/ hyperactivity disorders (ADHD) and with a range of such behavioral difficulties as oppositional defiant disorder (ODD) and conduct disorders. Some of the canine-assisted play therapy interventions used with these populations are described below.

CHILDREN WITH ATTENTION-DEFICIT/ HYPERACTIVITY DISORDER

Many of the canine play therapy interventions described in previous sections can be applied with children with ADHD as well. In particular, interventions involving dog training, grooming and calming, and emotional and behavioral regulation work well. Some additional ideas are described here.

Running With the Dogs. Heidi Kaduson (personal communication, December 9, 2006) uses an activity with children with ADHD and with Asperger's Syndrome that involves the children running with one of her Chihuahuas. The object of the game is for all of them to stop on cue, as the dog does. The game is similar to the popular children's game "Red Light-Green Light" but involves the dog. It can be used with individual children as well as small groups.

Slow Motion. In a similar intervention, a dog who has been trained to walk slowly on the cue, "Sloooowwwwww Moooootionnnn," plays along with the children. The children and dog can run as they please until the cue is given. Then all walk in the direction of the therapist in slow motion. This can be taken a step further by using the cue "Stay" or "Statues" (provided the dog has been taught this). Upon this cue, the children are to stop moving entirely and assume whatever position they are in, as if they were statues. The dog is trained to cease motion, too.

> The Slow Motion Game arose from an idiosyncrasy of Kirrie's. When we first played ball with her, she hated to see the game end. When she detected our body language that she interpreted as the end of the game, rather than running back with the ball, she walked back in slow motion, all the time assuming the typical crouch position of Border Collies when they are herding sheep. Although I subsequently refined her training so that she would run back when called, I permitted her slow motion walk whenever she was tired herself. I began associating the cue "Slow Motion" with her unusual gait, and she learned to walk that way on cue. Children and their parents have been very amused by this game. Both of the games above help children gain better control of their energies and bodies.

Both nondirective and directive canine play therapy interventions can be used successfully with these children. Kirrie has also "written letters" to children giving them tips on how to manage some of their ADHD symptoms. She is a credible source of information for the children, as they have seen her exceptionally high energy levels first-hand.

> When Kirrie – and I – first learned to use the "Look!" command, she wrote about it to an ADHD child as a tip for use at home:

> > "I've been learning some new commands. Risë learned some new things about Border Collies and how to train them. Now, when she wants to get my attention, she first says, 'Look!' and points to her eyes. At first, I thought she was kinda nuts. But now I understand that I'm supposed to look at her

eyes when she says that. Then I wait for what comes next. It seems to help me listen better, and then I don't get into so much trouble – everyone is happier, including me! Interesting, huh?? Maybe we could try an experiment, and you could get your mom to try something like that with you. Then you and I can compare notes. What d'you think about that idea?"

I shared the note with both the child and the mother, and they decided to work out their own signal. Kirrie and I followed through to see how it had worked for them, and both reported that the child was listening better when the mother first gave the verbal and hand signals they had selected. Kirrie, of course, was ecstatic and wrote the child a congratulatory note. The mother told me that the imagery of the dog's "Look!" command had actually helped her remember to use the signals more frequently and consistently.

Clicker training can sometimes provide activity and focus for children with ADHD. The therapist can practice the techniques with them using the "training game" described in Loar and Colman (2004) before involving the dog. The therapist should be prepared, however, for some rapid-fire clicking that might need facilitation (a caution from actual experience with a 6-year-old).

CHILDREN WITH
BEHAVIOR PROBLEMS

Here, too, many of the interventions described previously can be useful. Some additional approaches are described below.

Canines have been used in juvenile justice settings, as well as in adult prisons, to provide attachment experiences, a sense of purpose, new skills, and satisfaction with a job that contributes to others' well-being. These programs have been featured on news and television programs and typically involve the detained children in dog training. Some programs permit the dogs to live with the child, and the child is responsible for all of the dog's care and training. Programs last from a few months to a year or more. The children learn obedience training and conduct it on a regular basis. Some of the canines are earmarked for further service training and work, such as guide dogs for the blind or search-and-rescue dogs. Other programs have used dogs brought in from animal shelters who need training to make them more "adoptable."

Children who were interviewed in several televised programs over the past 5 years or so have consistently spoken of the deep, positive relationship they developed with the dog, and the boost to their self-esteem that occurred as they saw the outcomes of their new skills (e.g., Bondarenko, 2007; Loar & Colman, 2004).

Play therapist Judy Dawley (personal communication, January 4, 2007) reports how the use of her German Shorthair Pointer play therapy dog, Bria, helped break through the resistant demeanor of an adolescent girl. The girl had attachment problems and a difficult history, and she had frustrated other therapists in the past. She announced during her first meeting with the therapist, "I don't know you, I don't trust you, and I don't want to be here," and then walked out. The dog was present at the next meeting. Although the girl entered the session with the same attitude, it instantly changed when she saw the dog. She jumped out of her chair to go see the dog, saying, "I love dogs!" She petted the dog, and the therapist showed her the tricks the dog could do. In their third session, they jointly taught Bria to roll over, and the teen was much more engaged in therapy. By the fourth session, the girl took Bria into the playroom after which she asked the therapist to play a game with her. The adolescent conversed and laughed during the game, with all signs of resistance gone. The girl then began to discuss and work on issues of safety.

Heidi Kaduson (personal communication, December 9, 2006) starts all play therapy sessions for children with oppositional defiant disorder (ODD) with "doggie time." The children usually have the Chihuahuas sit on their laps, and when the dogs lick them and interact with them, the children laugh with delight. In addition, when children see the three dogs roughhousing and playing together, they learn that "just playing" helps the dogs calm down, a lesson they might be able to apply to themselves. These experiences cut through all opposition, and the children's play sessions continue smoothly.

These examples clearly show the social lubricant effect of dogs within the therapy environment. They create a friendly climate that engages children, reduces the underlying anxieties that usually drive oppositional behavior, and helps children relax through touch and laughter. The presence of dogs also gives the therapist a tacit recommendation as being an "okay" person.

Janey and Jimmy, ages 6 and 8 respectively, were very distressed when they went to live with their maternal grandparents. Their father was serving a prison sentence, and their mother was actively abusing drugs. Their distress showed in oppositional behavior. The grandparents were frustrated with their inability to find a positive way to interact with the children, and a school counselor referred them for play therapy. The primary intervention used was Filial Therapy, and the children enjoyed the special play sessions that their grandparents held with them. This family play intervention reduced the children's anxiety, strengthened their attachment with their grandparents, and reduced their oppositional behaviors significantly. Nevertheless, their mother called periodically, usually when she was high, and regardless of whether the children spoke with her, the calls were upsetting. The calls were often followed by several days of tension and acting out.

The grandparents were aware of Kirrie and asked if we could involve her. They said the children loved their mixed breed pet dog. I used Kirrie with the family just three times, after the filial play sessions had shifted to home. The grandparents reported on their home play sessions for the first part of the meeting while the children played in the waiting area. The rest of the session involved the entire family with Kirrie. We did some basic obedience training that the grandparents then initiated at home with their own dog. The children petted Kirrie and played some games with her. While they were playing, I told them how much Kirrie liked it when people took care of her. We also talked about their dog, Ragsy, and how much she might like it if they took care of her like they did with Kirrie. We developed a family plan in which the children interacted more with Ragsy and took turns feeding him. The grandparents supervised all interactions at home, and they incorporated a more playful way of enlisting the children's help, modeled on the way we had all interacted with Kirrie.

We then implemented a strategy at home to handle the mother's phone calls. Within a day of an upsetting call, the grandparents each held a play session with one of the children, and they encouraged the children to pet and talk with the dog. They also read some therapeutic stories at bedtime and engaged in calming activities. The children gave belly rubs to help Ragsy calm down, and then the grandparents gave the children backrubs to help them calm down. The family's distress was substantially relieved.

COMMUNICATION
AND SOCIAL ANXIETIES

*They [dogs] never talk about themselves but listen to you while you
talk about yourself, and keep up an appearance of being interested
in the conversation.*

-Jerome K. Jerome

Dogs seem to invite communication and relationship from people,
and especially children. It has been well documented that children talk
to their companion animals regularly (Jalongo, 2004; Melson, 2001;
Serpell, 2000). It seems natural then, that canine play therapy can be
used to assist with problems in these areas. Several applications are
described that show the use of a canine play therapist to assist with
speech and language development, stuttering and shyness, and related
communication difficulties.

When I was in 5th grade, one of my classmates had an obvious
cleft palate that set him apart from other students. He also had learning
difficulties that seemed to ostracize him. He became the focus of
mean-spirited jokes and teasing on the playground. His family bred
Great Pyrenees dogs, and one day our teacher invited him to bring a
couple of his dogs to school for show-and-tell. This usually reticent
boy stood before the class and told us many facts about the breed
and demonstrated how he trained them for dog shows. He seemed
poised and confident, unlike we had ever seen him before. During his
demonstration, I admired how much he knew about the dogs and
how well he managed these huge animals. They seemed to respect
him, and it was clear that he loved them. His "victim" persona was
nowhere to be seen.

I was not the only one who was impressed. As far as I knew, from
that day forward, the other students treated him with greater respect.
The teasing lessened or stopped – I was never aware of it happening
again, as I had been prior to this time. The change that I witnessed
remains clear in my mind 44 years later. From my current vantage
point, I think back upon this teacher with even greater admiration
than I felt for him at the time. He encouraged the boy to share his
own area of expertise with his peers, a behavioral demonstration that
showed the class that they really did not know the depths and talents
of this student. I suspect that that single experience, capitalizing on

the boy's strengths, not only changed our perceptions of our classmate, but also helped him reframe his self-image vis a vis his peers.

SPEECH AND LANGUAGE DEVELOPMENT

Children with language difficulties sometimes feel reluctant to speak aloud, perhaps because adults have worked so hard to help them improve their speech that they fear failure or because siblings or peers have teased them. It might be easier for these children to speak to dogs who do not criticize and who respond more to tone than actual words anyway. Dogs can be used in the play therapy context to help these children develop their language skills and to feel more relaxed about verbal and nonverbal communication. Canine play therapy is in no way a substitute for professional speech and language interventions, and the therapist should coordinate all efforts through the language specialist, if one is involved.

One way to reduce the speech pressures children feel is to provide them with a place where no one expects them to talk. In most forms of play therapy, children are permitted to communicate as they feel most comfortable, through their play. Spoken language is optional. When children become focused on their play, it is quite common for them to speak spontaneously, either through the imaginary characters they create or to clarify something with the therapist. With a therapy dog present, they have another avenue through which they can express themselves as they choose, verbally or nonverbally. Because the therapist initially prepares children to interact with the dog by teaching them some of the cues that the dog knows, children often are willing to speak to the dog to get it to do something they want.

A somewhat more directive way to involve the dog in children's language acquisition is to focus more heavily on the training interactions. The therapist teaches the child the simple statements that are used as cues and social reinforcers for the dog, models them, and then asks the child to try. Because the focus is on the dog's behavior, children feel less self-conscious. Consultation with a speech therapist can provide valuable information about what phonemes are relevant to the child's therapy so that the dog training can emphasize cues that use them the most. It is very useful to train the therapy dog to respond to both verbal and hand signals, so if the child's speech and intonation are exceptionally unclear, the therapist can stand behind the child and provide hand signals to the dog, backing up the child's attempt with verbal cues.

Becca was 2½ years old when her mother brought her to therapy for behavior problems. I noticed that she did not speak much, and when she did, it was very difficult to understand her. Her receptive language seemed normal, as she responded to requests and directions. She had not seen a speech therapist at that time. The behavior problems seemed to stem from the recent divorce of her parents and her father's move across the country. She also became frustrated when people did not understand her and asked her to repeat things. I used Filial Therapy to help with the family and behavioral issues. Becca enjoyed the play sessions and played out themes relevant to her problem although she rarely spoke. Her mother was able to empathically listen to Becca's feelings during the play and engaged in imaginary play when Becca nonverbally indicated that she should. Limits were rare, but Becca's mother improved in her firmness and consistency when needed.

Becca saw Kirrie at the office one day and eagerly reached out to pet her. I decided to add a canine play therapy component to our meetings. For 10 minutes after each parent-child play session and my subsequent feedback discussion with Becca's mother, I taught Becca how to give cues to Kirrie and to play with her. Her mother stayed with us and observed. The child-canine interactions took place in the context of playing ball with Kirrie. I taught Becca how to toss the ball, call Kirrie back to her ("Come!), tell Kirrie to place the ball in her hand ("Hand!"), and then tell Kirrie to "Sit!" Becca learned quickly and gave the verbal cues unselfconsciously. She clearly enjoyed being in charge of the game. After three sessions with Kirrie, her mother reported that Becca had begun vocalizing much more frequently at home, and that she was attempting to pronounce more words. Her speech and language development proceeded at a faster pace, but I did suggest a consult with a speech therapist, too.

SHYNESS AND STUTTERING

Shyness, stuttering, and similar difficulties usually are associated with significant social anxiety. Shy children frequently communicate little or not at all with others for fear of being rejected or thought poorly of. Children who stutter usually report that the more they focus on trying to control their stuttering, the worse it becomes. These children often are anxious and self-conscious, and many engage in comparative thinking processes, evaluating themselves socially as less adequate than their siblings or peers. Play therapy is valuable to help these children enact and master their social fears, and adding canines has several benefits. First, the children's focus is drawn to the dog rather than themselves. Second, dogs are not self-conscious creatures, and they can be quite comical. The therapist can lightly point this out and encourage the child to engage in playful activities with the dog. Third, as children play with the human and canine play therapists, they learn that they are not being judged. Once they feel that acceptance, they become more open to simply enjoy the freedom of being themselves. It allows them the experience of being silly or goofy and to see that it has benefits. Although transfer to human relationships is not automatic, once children have a frame of reference for playfulness, they are more likely to take a few more risks with some of their peers.

The use of canines in play therapy for shy children or children who stutter is often coupled with social skills and family support interventions. Role plays with a canine therapist seem to add a further dimension of safety while learning and practicing new social behaviors.

Another intervention for these children can be employed from the home setting, especially if the family has a dog. During a "Sociology of the Family" course at the University of Pennsylvania many years ago, the professor, Dr. Tony Campolo, suggested that one of the most effective ways of helping a stuttering child would be to ask the child to walk the family dog (if they had one) regularly. He asked the students to think what happens when a child is out in a safe, friendly neighborhood walking a dog. People (at least dog lovers) often stop and ask questions about the dog. They look at the dog, pet the dog, and often make a fuss. With the adults' attention focused on the dog, it becomes easier for the child to communicate.

Of course, this intervention was suggested to the class at a time when communities were more connected and parents could entrust their children's safety to the watchful eye of neighbors. Nowadays, such an intervention should be applied only with great caution, as it would not be a feasible approach in many neighborhoods due to safety or social isolation factors. Some neighborhoods simply are not safe for a child to walk alone. In others, neighbors do not know each other and do not talk casually in this manner. Furthermore, parents wisely train their children to avoid speaking to strangers to avoid victimization. Even so, there are times when such an intervention could be used, or the parents could help arrange for the child to take the dog to a social or extended family event where the parents could monitor the situation.

> Thirteen-year-old Nick was very shy in social situations. His usually mild stuttering became much more pronounced when he was with other children his own age. His parents had recently bought him a Golden Retriever puppy for his birthday, and he was participating with its training and care. An outdoor family reunion was planned for August, when the puppy would be 6 months old. The dog was well behaved and friendly with children. During a session with Nick and his parents, we discussed the ramifications of taking the puppy to the reunion and having Nick be in charge of walking and playing with it. Complete plans for the dog's care were made, including ways to provide it with a cool shelter and place to sleep. Nick was excited when he came for the session following the reunion. He told me he was "the most popular person there!" His parents said the dog was a hit with the cousins, aunts, and uncles, and Nick received much more attention than usual because he was the "puppy master." Although he still stuttered when he spoke with his relatives, they noted that it had not worsened as it usually did when he communicated with people outside the immediate family. They were so encouraged by Nick's boost of social confidence from this event that they were planning to take the puppy on several other planned family outings.

Another approach for reticent children involves talking with the dog directly. The child can be encouraged to whisper to the dog, tell stories to the dog, or ask the therapist to share "dog stories" about the canine play therapist with the child. Children can also write letters and draw pictures for the dog and receive replies from the canine/human therapy team. Several of the canine interventions covered in other sections of this monograph would also apply to this population of children. Essentially any intervention that engages the child's interest and communicative abilities while focusing attention primarily on the canine has potential for helping reduce the child's self-consciousness while at the same time encouraging communication and interaction.

OTHER COMMUNICATION AND SOCIAL DIFFICULTIES

Canine-assisted play therapy has potential benefits for other types of communication and social problems. Temple Grandin (Grandin &

Johnson, 2005) describes how relationships with animals helped her overcome much of the isolation and difficulties associated with her own autism as a teenager, and she has described fascinating similarities between individuals with autism and animals in terms of how they think, feel, and behave. Her work has implications for possible development in animal-assisted play therapy. A meta-analysis of AAT research showed clear benefits for individuals with Pervasive Developmental Disorder (PDD; Nimer & Lundahl, 2007). Well-known psychologist and play therapist Heidi Kaduson (personal communication, February 10, 2007) has used her three Chihuahuas with children with PDD. She follows regular play sessions with 5 minutes of playing with the dogs. She has found that, typically, the children overcome their fear of dogs within four sessions.

Play therapy often is quite valuable for the treatment of selective mutism, especially because it is largely nonverbal and removes pressures to communicate verbally. With less attention given to their verbal communication, many selectively mute children in play therapy begin to whisper or use more language in their play and with the therapist after just a few sessions, and their speaking seems to generalize to other situations such as school. The use of a canine-play therapist can facilitate this process. Heidi Kaduson (personal communication, February 10, 2007) has found that the antics of her Chihuahuas have helped selectively mute children laugh, thus breaking through their mutism.

I have used canines with selectively mute children in two ways. One is to include the dog in the nondirective play sessions but without any suggestion for the child to play with the dog. I might say, "This is a very special playroom. You can do just about anything you want in here. If there's something you may not do, I'll let you know. It's up to you whether you talk or not – you don't have to – and it's up to you whether or not you play with the dog. Here's where she will be and some of the things you can use with her if you decide to." Invariably the children have shown interest in the dog and often interact with her right away. They speak to the dog before long, and then this extends to me, often in the form of questions about the dog.

The other way that I have used the dog is in the context of more directive play therapy interventions. I tell the children how to "communicate" with the dog through gestures, whispers, whistles, and words and let the children complete whatever activity I have planned with the dog using whichever form of communication they wish. Frequently, the children begin to speak to the dog after they see how I do it. With the attention on the dog, the focus is no longer on the children's production of speech, and they voluntarily begin to use language more often.

CANINE READING PROGRAMS

Outside of a dog, a book is man's best friend. Inside of a dog it's too dark to read.
                        -Groucho Marx

Therapy dogs have been used successfully to improve children's reading skills (Jalongo, 2004). Children read aloud to dogs who are trained to "listen" attentively. The use of a dog can reduce the stress associated with academic tasks, thereby promoting greater interest and success with reading. Canine reading can be used to help children with speech and language problems, self-consciousness, and general communication difficulties, also. In play therapy, this approach can be adapted to the reading of therapeutic stories and books (e.g., those offered through www.childtherapytoys.com; www.selfesteemshop.com). Since many of the therapeutic books used in bibliotherapy are told from the animals' points of view, children seem to enjoy reading them to animals. The focus here is not on reading skills but on helping children through metaphors, but both aims can be reached through the same activity. Jalongo (2004) provides many resources on animal-assisted programs for reading that can easily be incorporated into therapeutic work.

DOGGIE DRESS-UP

If you are a dog and your owner suggests that you wear a sweater, suggest that he wear a tail.
                        -Fran Lebowitz

Doggie Dress-Up is a combination of dramatic play therapy, behavioral rehearsal, and canine-assisted therapy. It is helpful for shy children and others with social difficulties. It can be used with a child alone or with a small group of two or three children.

In Doggie Dress-Up, the therapist helps the children develop a scenario or stage-play that they can enact with the dog's help. The scenario is related to the child's difficulties, at least symbolically, and sometimes more directly. The children then select their own costumes and props. The therapist shows children some choices of dress-up items that they may select for the dog, usually in the form of bandannas or other items that can fit easily over the dog's neck or attach to the collar. (Although there are many "outfits" that one can purchase for dogs, including an increasingly wide range of Halloween costumes, the therapist should remember that most dogs do not enjoy being confined in clothing. If the costume or activity is not enjoyable for the dog, it should not be used. Some of the neck scarves available in craft stores work well as a simple costume, such as a flowered pattern for a princess dog, a camouflage print for a military dog, or a bright orange bandanna for a hunting dog. A wide range of theme-related bandannas useful for play therapy work are also available at www.k9design.com.). After the children and the canine are attired, the therapist facilitates the children's and the dog's acting out the scene.

Using this method, the therapist can help children enact scenes relating to almost any imaginable social situation, such as friendship, assertiveness, arguments, rejection, and so on. The overall process and debriefing remain lighthearted.

Amber was 11 years old and had been referred by her teacher because she had recently withdrawn from her classmates, and her school work had suffered. She had revealed to her mother that her best friend throughout elementary school had stopped talking to her for no apparent reason. Amber's mother tried to encourage her to develop other friendships, but Amber had been so hurt by her friend's rejection that she was reluctant to do so.

Amber told me in our first meeting that she wanted to be an actress someday, and after a few sessions, I introduced her to Corky, one of our Beagles. Corky never minded being dressed up in minor ways. As one of our play therapy interventions, we developed a scene that related to Amber's feelings of sadness and rejection. Amber suggested the storyline, which resembled that of Cinderella, but featured a female wizard (Amberella) and her magical dog (Corkyella). Corkyella had the magical ability to tell if people were "for real" or if they were phonies. Amber dressed up in a princess dress and a wizard hat, and we put a loose-fitting bandanna with a blue background and yellow "wizard stars" around Corky's neck. Amberella and Corkyella then wandered throughout the land (playroom) meeting many people (dolls). In each case, Amberella told Corkyella what characteristics to look for to determine if the people were sincere. Corkyella would then confirm this information with a bark (which I prompted). Amberella cast spells on those deemed insincere, often turning them into inanimate objects.

After Amber seemed to regain some confidence from this role play, I suggested that she and I play the "Wizard Game," a variation of Kaduson's *News Network* (Kaduson, 2006) while Corky took a nap. In this cognitive-behavioral play therapy technique, Amber, continuing in her role of Amberella, answered questions about friendship and trust from a variety of animal puppets, which I played. After several sessions, Amber was able to confront her friend appropriately and to focus on other friendships. The play with Corky seemed to facilitate her progress by helping her open up, feel accepted, and begin problem solving. I was able to follow through with other play therapy and behavioral interventions that led to rapid progress.

CANINE-ASSISTED
SOCIAL SKILLS GROUPS

Social skills training or play therapy groups are commonly used to help children with their social interactions. Canines can assist with group social skills interventions, too. Some of the same training or play activities mentioned elsewhere in this monograph can be used with small groups of children. The children can learn canine body language and play games in which they identify the meaning of different expressions. Children can compare canine and human facial expressions through the use of photographs of each. They can use clicker training with each other to read and respond to social cues and to give positive feedback.

Children can also learn to interact as a group with a therapy dog. They learn to take turns, avoid crowding the dog, communicate with the dog, create a set of "doggie rules," and share their experiences with the dog with each other. The use of a therapy dog during some of the social skills sessions adds fun, relevance, and a source of common interest to the process.

FAMILIES AND THE FUTURE

Against the assault of laughter nothing can stand.
-Mark Twain

FAMILY INVOLVEMENT

This monograph has included relatively little information about families, yet they are probably the most critical factor influencing the ultimate success of any type of treatment. Family relationships provide potent means for all family members to learn about, explore, and define themselves. When families function well, they are a vital source of support and encouragement. When biological families are unable to provide adequate safety and structure, sometimes extended family members, foster families, and adoptive families step in to help those most vulnerable to trauma and neglect – the children. Although therapists can help children and families move in healthy directions, their impact is limited by the frequency and nature of therapy. Involvement of the entire family is essential to play therapy, whether the therapist consults and works with parents outside the play sessions or involves them intimately in the process as in Filial Therapy.

When canines are incorporated into the play therapy process, family members can be involved in a number of ways. The therapist initially should discuss all aspects of the canine program, including benefits and risks, with parents before starting. Parents need to give their consent to animal involvement that goes beyond the mere presence of the dog in the office. Although parents need not be present for many of the canine-assisted interventions, there are times when they can take part as observers or participants. In particular, they can watch and participate when the therapist prepares the child to meet the dog. Many parents are unaware of the proper ways to approach canines, and they can benefit from this knowledge themselves as well as support their child's future interactions with family, neighborhood, and unfamiliar dogs.

When children have mastered some of the basic training methods, they can demonstrate them for their parents during a session. It is useful for the therapist to develop an understanding of the parents' attitudes about dogs and dog training methods to ensure that the parents will be supportive of the child's demonstrations. Alternatively, when the therapist invites the parents to watch the child-canine demonstrations, he or she can prepare the parents for what they will see and what types of responses would be helpful to their child.

Some of the therapist-directed play interventions can include parents or entire families, as well. For example, the entire family might complete a special sandtray or jointly create a memory book to share their feelings about the loss of their dog. One therapist asked a family to dress up in costumes and hold a "party" to honor their deceased Spaniel. Then the entire family drew pictures of their happy memories and wrote messages to the dog on a collective family collage. Many other interventions included here can incorporate family members quite readily.

Another family intervention involves transferring some of the skills the children have learned in their canine-assisted play sessions to their own pets at home. This process depends a great deal on the therapist's dog handling, training, and behavior consultation skills. With the proper background, the therapist might invite the family to bring one of their dogs into the session, or the therapist might make a home visit to help the transfer of skills. Boundary considerations are important to avoid any conflict of interest when doing this. More commonly, the therapist can discuss with the child and parents the use of various training and play activities with the family pets. This discussion should include ample information about the pet's temperament and personality so that the skill transfer can be tailored to an animal that might be quite different from the play therapy dog. To be safe and ethical, this type of family involvement should be undertaken only by people with significant dog behavior consultation training and skills and with prior consideration of potential dual roles or conflicts of interest. Otherwise, if the family is experiencing problems with their dog, they can be referred to a local trainer or behavior professional. Hoover's (2006) book is a very useful resource in this area, with a family development perspective on dog behavior consulting. Pelar's (2005) book is a family-friendly guide that can be recommended to parents. Loar and Colman (2004) describe clicker training with families to encourage change.

> Josh, whom we have met in earlier case examples, was in foster care when he first began working and playing with Kirrie. He was very proud of his new skills, and his foster mother told me that his behavior with her dog had been much more appropriate after he began learning and interacting with Kirrie. After several sessions, Josh was able to use various obedience cues and praise very well. He was excited to

show what he had learned to his foster mother. This usually quiet boy animatedly explained each of the cues he was demonstrating and showed her each one several times. She was also pleased. Josh had never done well at school, nor was he involved in many activities, so this was one of the first times he was able to show his success in such a visible, concrete way. During the demonstration, he commented, "You always have to tell Kirrie she's doing a good job because she might forget and be bad." His foster mother replied, "Sounds just like someone I know!" He grinned and said, "Yep!"

FINAL SUGGESTIONS

Canine-assisted play therapy has potential for great success and great failure. A few considerations are worth keeping in mind.

- Avoid overcontrolling the process. Think "empowerment" and permit children and canines to find their own unique relationship without interference. The therapist is there to facilitate the process, not to control it.
- Consider carefully the expectations that are being placed on the dogs. It is easy to take advantage of their accommodating natures without intending to. Vigilance about stress and fatigue levels is important.
- Remember that the therapist provides a role model to children in the ways to interact and treat dogs. All behaviors during canine-assisted play therapy should demonstrate to children how they can interact safely and happily with dogs throughout their lives.
- Similarly, remember that children watch how the therapist treats the dog. The therapist's respectful relationship with the dog can carry much meaning to children about the type of relationship they can expect from the therapist.
- After all the training and planning, relax and let the canine cotherapists do their thing. Spontaneity yields many therapeutic opportunities.
- Focus on the relationships. It is not so much the specific activities that matter, as the relationships that children form – with the dog, with the therapist, and with their families. Therapists' relationships with their dogs, the children, and the families are

all interwoven into the change process. Playfulness is an important part of healthy attachment.

INTO THE FUTURE: RESEARCH AND DEVELOPMENT OF CANINE-ASSISTED PLAY THERAPY

> *The plural of anecdote is data.*
> -Marc Bekoff

The approach used in this book is grounded in the well-established fields of animal-assisted therapy and play therapy. Its foundations are rooted in the research on human-animal bonds, animal and human play, animal-assisted therapy, and play therapy. There are countless case studies attesting to its effectiveness, and they should not be dismissed. Clinical reports are promising, including spontaneous positive assessments by therapy "end-users," that is, parents, foster care agencies, teachers, and children. VanFleet's (2007b) study of 83 play therapists who incorporate animals into their work found unanimous and enthusiastic praise for the outcomes. Nearly all respondents shared anecdotes of animals who helped them break through to oppositional, resistant children or helped anxious children learn to relax and laugh, thereby enhancing play therapy progress.

Another study of children's perceptions of the play therapy process is underway, part of which involves children completing three sandtrays at the end of therapy to show what was helpful, what was not helpful, and their wishes for their future. Several therapists who use dogs some of the time are participating, and one of the measures involves the frequency with which children select canine miniatures for this activity (the therapists are unaware of the measures and simply take photographs of the sandtrays and record the children's explanations). A pilot study of 21 children showed that all 11 of the children in the canine-assisted play therapy group placed a dog miniature in their "liked best" sandtray, whereas only 2 of the 10 children in the play therapy-only group selected miniature dogs. By itself, not many conclusions can be drawn from this, but all sources of information gathered in these early stages of empirical inquiry will help guide more controlled research in the future. Thompson (2007) is currently conducting the first known controlled study of the use of canines in nondirective play therapy.

Of course, more rigorous research is needed. Case studies by enthusiastic therapists, although informative and potentially valuable for qualitative analysis, are filled with potential biases. This monograph has been written to provide a description of methods that have excited many clinicians and the children and families they treat. It represents the starting point for the development of this integrated therapeutic approach, both clinically and empirically. It is hoped that it will encourage more practitioners to obtain training in this area and spur more open dialog about the use of canines and other animals in play therapy. Good ideas become better ideas only through frank discussion and sharing of ideas and concerns. It is hoped that as the field grows and training programs develop, research questions will be refined and more rigorous studies can be conducted.

Clinicians have been involving animals in their work in varying degrees for many years. From Freud's Chows to Levinson's Jingles to VanFleet's menagerie, it is likely that practitioners will continue to seek ways to share the joys experienced in their own pet dog relationships with clients who might benefit from a bit more laughter and an accepting relationship in the form of a slurpy tongue.

APPENDICES

Appendix A

Sample Introductory Letter
From a Play Therapy Dog to a Child

*(Written on special stationery featuring
the dog's photograph and a playful font.)*

Dear _____,

Hi! My name is Kirrie, and I want to introduce myself to you. I'm part Border Collie and part Beagle. I am a play therapy dog. I love to play and I love to be with kids. The best thing ever is getting to play with kids.

I had a rough start in life. Nobody seemed to want me. I went into doggie foster care (called a rescue), and then I was adopted by Risë and her family. I am very happy now. Border Collie dogs really like to work, so Risë has trained me how to do some work with kids. That's why I'm writing to you.

Sometimes I work at the Beech Street Program. It's up to the kids whether they want to meet me. I'm really very sweet. I try to behave like a good dog, but sometimes I have some little behavior problems that I need help with. Sometimes the kids at the Beech Street Program can help me with them. They help train me. Risë can show you how to do that. Mostly I behave myself pretty well, though. I never hurt anyone, and I really try hard. (One of my worst problems is that I love to rip up paper towels in tiny little pieces all over the floor!)

If you would like to meet me and play with me, you can tell them at the Beech Street Program. Risë will meet with you first to show you some great ways to say hello to me, and she will also give you some dog cookies that you can give to me when we first meet. I LOVE that!!

Here's a picture of me in the playroom (picture is included of Kirrie watching the puppet theater). I was waiting for a puppet show to begin. I guess that's all for now. I hope that we get to meet some day!

Kirrie

Appendix B

Sample Letter From Kirrie,
<u>A Play Therapy Dog to Play Therapists</u>

Dear Play Therapy Colleagues,

By now you've learned that I'm a play therapy dog. I hope you get excited and decide to learn more about this and maybe even try it someday! I know it has given me an outlet for all my energy and also a new purpose to my life. I know that the play therapists all thought they had it sewn up – playing for a living – but now some of us canines are onto this good thing. So look out! You'll be seeing more of us hanging around play therapy rooms before you know it!

It hasn't always been easy for me. There's a lot to learn, and I sometimes get distracted by all the other things going on around me. But with lots of practice and reinforcement and patience and fun, I know I'm going to get it! It's really fun to be teamed up with a play therapist and to see how much the kids and families like to have me around some of the time. (Also, since I'm an expert on play, one of the best rewards that I get from my play therapy work is to go home and get to play ball – "PB" – until I drop!)

I wanted to give you future play therapy dog handlers a few tips or things to think about. Even though the kids really like me and focus on me, you are very important, too. In addition to making sure that the child and I get along and everyone stays safe, I'm going to suggest some other things that you might need to do.

Here are the things that therapist/handlers need to do sometimes:

- Structure the overall situation.
- Match canine play therapy interventions to BOTH the child's needs/goals AND the dog's abilities and energy levels.
- Use your creativity to come up with new ideas of how to incorporate us – one way is to just watch us (the pets) and the fun and funny things we do in order to give you some new ideas.

- Let the dogs know that they're doing a good job, right while they're doing it and at the end.
- Let the kids know that they're doing a good job, especially if they're learning to train the dogs.
- Make some facilitative comments (I'm not sure what that word means, but I hear it a lot) to help the child understand the "bigger picture" of what's happening during the canine-assisted play therapy.
- Use your empathy freely. As a dog, of course, I know quite a lot about empathy. I believe that it's important for all your work, even when the play therapy dogs are around to give it, too!
- Make sure that the child doesn't get overwhelmed. Sometimes they can get anxious or overly excited around us, so they might need to start with smaller doses of us at first.
- Make sure that we play therapy dogs don't get too stressed. This is actually hard work for us, so we need you to learn our signals and keep your eye on how we're doing, too.
- Along with that, get to know us as dogs and accept us for who and what we are. We aren't people, but we do have a lot to offer the people we work with. You do the people part, and we'll do the canine part, okay?
- You'll have to juggle a lot of information at once when you're working with us. You'll need to keep an eye on things to make sure they go well, but you don't want to overcontrol the situation. That gives the kids and us the sense that you don't trust us. (Plus it makes us very nervous if you're nervous!) If you get anxious about what's happening, maybe you can do a little more training with us, get a helper, or something else to take the pressure off.

Well, I know there's more that I could tell you, but that's it for now. That should get you started so that things don't get too RUFF for you in your work (RUFF, get it??). Now, be a luv and pass me the cookies, okay?

Your Pooch in Play,

Kirrie

REFERENCES

Adams, D. L. (1997). Animal-assisted enhancement of speech therapy: A case study. *Anthrozoös, 10*(1), 53-56.

Allen, C., & Bekoff, M. (2005). Animal play and the evolution of morality: An ethological approach. *Topoi, 24*, 125-135.

Altschuler, E. L. (1999). Pet-facilitated therapy for posttraumatic stress disorder. *Annals of Clinical Psychiatry, 11*(1), 29-30.

American Kennel Club. (1996). *The Complete Dog Book for Kids.* New York: Wiley.

American Kennel Club. (2006). *The Complete Dog Book* (20th ed.). New York: Ballantine Books.

American Psychological Association. (2002). Ethical principles of psychologists and code of conduct. *American Psychologist, 57*, 1060-1073.

Ascione, F. R. (1992). Enhancing children's attitudes about the humane treatment of animals: Generalisation to human-directed empathy. *Anthrozoös, 5*, 176-191.

Ascione, F. R., & Weber, C. V. (1996). Children's attitudes about the humane treatment of animals and empathy: One year follow up of a school-based intervention. *Anthrozoös, 9*, 188-195.

Barker, S. B., & Barker, R. T. (1988). The human-canine bond: Closer than family ties? *Journal of Mental Health Counseling, 10*(1), 46-56.

Beck, A. M., & Katcher, A. H. (1996). *Between Pets and People: The Importance of Animal Companionship* (rev. ed.). West Lafayette, IN: Purdue University Press.

Beck, A. M., & Katcher, A. H. (2003). Future directions in human-animal bond research. *American Behavioral Scientist, 47*(1), 79-93.

Becker, M., & Morton, D. (2002). *The Healing Power of Pets: Harnessing the Amazing Ability of Pets to Make and Keep People Happy and Healthy.* New York: Hyperion.

Becker, M., & Spadafori. G. (2006). *Why Do Dogs Drink Out of the Toilet?* Deerfield Beach, FL: Health Communications.

Bekoff, M. (2004). Wild justice and fair play: Cooperation, forgiveness, and morality in animals. *Biology and Philosophy, 19,* 489-520.

Bekoff, M. (2006, July). Play fair. *Ranger Rick, 40*(7), 30-31.

Bekoff, M. (2007). *The Emotional Lives of Animals.* Novato, CA: New World Library.

Bekoff, M., & Byers, J. (Eds.). (1998). *Animal Play: Evolutionary, Comparative, and Ecological Perspectives.* New York: Cambridge University Press.

Belsky, J., & Nezworski, T. (Eds.). (1988). *Clinical Implications of Attachment.* Hillsdale, NJ: Lawrence Erlbaum.

Bielakiewicz, G. J. (2005). *The Only Dog Tricks Book You'll Ever Need: Impress Friends, Family – and Other Dogs!* Avon, MA: Adams Media.

Bonas, S., McNicholas, J., & Collis, G. (2000). Pets in the network of family relationships: An empirical study. In A. L. Podberscek, E. S. Paul, & J. A. Serpell (Eds.), *Companion Animals and Us: Exploring the Relationships Between People and Pets* (pp. 209-236). New York: Cambridge University Press.

Bondarenko, N. (2007). *BBC and Canine Partners: Helping At-Risk Children.* Unpublished manuscript.

Bratton, S. C., Ray, D., Rhine, T., & Jones, L. (2005). The efficacy of play therapy with children: A meta-analytic review of treatment outcomes. *Professional Psychology: Research and Practice, 36*(4), 376-390.

Brown, S. (1994). Animals at play. *National Geographic, 186*(6), 2-35.

Brown, S., & Kennard, D. (2000). *The Promise of Play* [Video series]. Santa Monica, CA: Direct Cinema Limited.

Burghardt, G. M. (2005). *The Genesis of Animal Play: Testing the Limits.* Cambridge, MA: The MIT Press.

Carpenter, M. L. (2005). Trying to bridge the gap: The traditional mental health professional and animal assisted therapy. *Equine Facilitated Mental Health Association Newsletter*, *Spring*, 6-7.

Chandler, C. K. (2005). *Animal Assisted Therapy in Counseling*. New York: Routledge.

Clark, K. E., & Ladd, G. W. (2000). Connectedness and autonomy support in parent-child relationships: Links to children's socioemotional orientation and peer relationships. *Developmental Psychology, 36*(4), 485-498.

Clutton-Brock, J. (1995). Origins of the dog: Domestication and early history. In J. Serpell (Ed.), *The Domestic Dog: Its Evolution, Behaviour, and Interactions With People* (pp. 7-20). New York: Cambridge University Press.

Darwin, C. (1872, reprinted 1965). *The Expression of the Emotions in Man and Animals.* Chicago: The University of Chicago Press. (Original work published 1872)

Davison, K. K., & Birch, L. L. (2001). Childhood overweight: A contextual model and recommendations for future research. *Obesity Reviews, 2*, 159-171.

Delta Society. (2004). *Team Training Course Manual: A Delta Society® Program for Animal-Assisted Activities and Therapy*. Bellevue, WA: Author.

Demas, C., & Hoyt, A. (2004). *Saying Goodbye to Lulu*. New York: Little, Brown and Company.

Dennison, P. S. (2005). *Bringing Light to Shadow: A Dog Trainer's Diary*. Wenatchee, WA: Dogwise Publishing.

Donaldson, J. (2005). *The Culture Clash* (2nd ed.). Berkeley, CA: James & Kenneth Publishers.

Douglas, D. K. (2006). *Benefits to Pets From the Human-Animal Bond: A Study of Pet Owner Behaviors and Their Relation to Attachment.* Ann Arbor, MI: ProQuest Company.

Dunbar, I. (1996a). *Dog Training for Children* [Video]. Berkeley, CA: James & Kenneth Publishers.

Dunbar, I. (1996b). *How to Teach a New Dog Old Tricks*. Berkeley, CA: James & Kenneth Publishers.

Elkind, D. (2007a). *The Hurried Child* (25th anniversary ed.). New York: Perseus.

Elkind, D. (2007b). *The Power of Play: How Imaginative, Spontaneous Activities Lead to Healthier and Happier Children.* New York: Perseus.

Fine, A. H. (Ed.). (2000). *Handbook on Animal-Assisted Therapy: Theoretical Foundations and Guidelines for Practice.* San Diego: Academic Press.

Fine, A. H. (Ed.). (2006). *Handbook on Animal-Assisted Therapy: Theoretical Foundations and Guidelines for Practice* (2nd ed.). San Diego: Academic Press.

Fleisherfilm. (1999). *Why Dogs Smile and Chimpanzees Cry* [DVD]. Silver Spring, MD: Devillier Donegan Enterprises.

Fox, M. W. (2004). *Healing Touch for Dogs: The Proven Massage Program for Dogs.* New York: Newmarket Press.

Fredrickson, M., & Howie, A. R. (2000). Methods, standards, guidelines, and considerations in selecting animals for animal-assisted therapy. In A. H. Fine (Ed.), *Handbook on Animal-Assisted Therapy: Theoretical Foundations and Guidelines for Practice* (pp. 99-114). San Diego: Academic Press.

Friedmann, E., Katcher, A. H., Thomas, S. A., Lynch, J. J., & Messent, P. R. (1983). Social interaction and blood pressure: Influence of animal companions. *Journal of Nervous and Mental Disease, 171,* 461-465.

Friedmann, E., Thomas, S. A., & Eddy, T. J. (2000). Companion animals and human health: Physical and cardiovascular influences. In A. L. Podberscek, E. S. Paul, & J. A. Serpell (Eds.), *Companion Animals and Us: Exploring the Relationships Between People and Pets* (pp. 125-142). New York: Cambridge University Press.

Gallo-Lopez, L. (2001). TV show storyboard. In H. G. Kaduson & C. E. Schaefer (Eds.), *101 More Favorite Play Therapy Techniques* (pp. 8-10). Northvale, NJ: Jason Aronson.

Gil, E. (1991). *The Healing Power of Play: Working With Abused Children.* New York: Guilford.

Ginsburg, K. R. (2007). The importance of play in promoting healthy child development and maintaining strong parent-child bonds. *Pediatrics, 119*(1), 182-191.

Golan, M., & Weizman, A. (2001). Familial approach to the treatment of childhood obesity: Conceptual mode. *Journal of Nutrition Education, 33,* 102-107.

Gonski, Y. A. (1985). The therapeutic utilization of canines in a child welfare setting. *Child and Adolescent Social Work Journal, 2,* 93-105.

Goodall, J., & Bekoff, M. (2002). *The Ten Trusts: What We Must Do to Care for the Animals We Love.* New York: Harper Collins (HarperSanFrancisco).

Gorczyca, K., Fine, A. H., Spain, C. V., Callaghan, D., Nelson, L., Popejoy, L., Wong, B., & Wong, S. (2006). History, development, and theory of human-animal support services for people with AIDS/HIV and other disabling chronic conditions. In A. H. Fine (Ed.), *Handbook on Animal-Assisted Therapy: Theoretical Foundations and Guidelines for Practice* (2nd ed., pp. 303-354). San Diego: Academic Press.

Grandin, T., & Johnson, C. (2005). *Animals in Translation.* Orlando, FL: A Harvest Book (Harcourt).

Greenbaum, S. D. (2006). Introduction to working with animal-assisted crisis response animal handler teams. *International Journal of Emergency Mental Health, 8*(1), 49-63.

Guerney, L. F. (1983). Introduction to filial therapy: Training parents as therapists. In P. A. Keller & L. G. Ritt (Eds.), *Innovations in Clinical Practice: A Source Book* (Vol. 2, pp. 26-39). Sarasota, FL: Professional Resource Exchange.

Guerney, L. F. (1991). A survey of self-supports and social supports of self-care children. *Elementary School Guidance and Counseling, 25*(4), 243-254.

Hanselman, J. L. (2001). Coping skills interventions with adolescents in anger management using animals in therapy. *Journal of Child and Adolescent Group Therapy, 11*(4), 159-195.

Hart, L. A. (1995). Dogs as human companions: A review of the relationship. In J. Serpell (Ed.), *The Domestic Dog: Its Evolution, Behaviour and Interactions With People* (pp. 161-178). New York: Cambridge University Press.

Hayden, A. J. (2005). An exploration of the experiences of adolescents who participated in equine-facilitated psychotherapy: A resiliency perspective. *Dissertation Abstracts International, Section B: The Sciences and Engineering, 65*(12-B), 6653.

Hobbs, V. (2006). *Sheep.* New York: Frances Foster Books (Farrar Straus Giroux).

Hodgson, S. (2001). *Dog Tricks for Dummies*. New York: Wiley.

Hoover, L. D. (2006). *The Family in Dog Behavior Consulting*. Pittsburgh, PA: Legand Publishing.

Jalongo, M. R. (Ed.). (2004). *The World's Children and Their Companion Animals: Developmental and Educational Significance of the Child/Pet Bond*. Olney, MD: Association for Childhood Education International.

Jalongo, M. R., Astorino, T., & Bomboy, N. (2004). Canine visitors: The influence of therapy dogs on young children's learning and well-being in classrooms and hospitals. *Early Childhood Education Journal, 32*(1), 9-16.

James, B. (1994). *Handbook for Treatment of Attachment-Trauma Problems in Children*. New York: The Free Press.

Jenkins, J. L. (1986). Physiological effects of petting a companion animal. *Psychological Reports, 58*(1), 21-22.

Kaduson, H. G. (2001). Broadcast news. In H. G. Kaduson & C. E. Schaefer (Eds.), *101 More Favorite Play Therapy Techniques* (pp. 397-400). Northvale, NJ: Jason Aronson.

Kaduson, H. G. (2006). *Play Therapy for Children With ADHD* [DVD]. Monroe Township, NJ: Author.

Kaduson, H. G., Cangelosi, D., & Schaefer, C. (Eds.). (1997). *The Playing Cure: Individualized Play Therapy for Specific Childhood Problems*. New York: Jason Aronson.

Kaduson, H. G., & Schaefer, C. E. (Eds.). (2000). *Short-Term Play Therapy for Children*. New York: Guilford.

Kaduson, H. G., & Schaefer, C. E. (Eds.). (2006). *Short-Term Play Therapy for Children* (Vol. 2). New York: Guilford.

Kalnajs, S. (2006a). *Am I Safe? The Art and Science of Canine Behavior Assessments*. Madison, WI: Blue Dog Training & Behavior.

Kalnajs, S. (2006b). *The Language of Dogs: Understanding Canine Body Language and Other Communication Signals* [DVD set]. Madison, WI: Blue Dog Training & Behavior.

Kaminski, M., Pellino, T., & Wish, J. (2002). Play and pets: The physical and emotional impact of child-life and pet therapy on hospitalized children. *Children's Health Care, 31*(4), 321-335.

Katz, J. (2003). *The New Work of Dogs: Tending to Life, Love, and Family*. New York: Random House.

Katz, J. (2005). *Katz on Dogs: A Commonsense Guide to Training and Living With Dogs*. New York: Random House.

Knapp, C. (1998). *Pack of Two: The Intricate Bond Between People and Dogs*. New York: Delta.

Kohr, G. C. (2006). *K-9 and Critical Stress Management*. Unpublished manuscript.

Kottman, T. (1995). *Partners in Play: An Adlerian Approach to Play Therapy*. Alexandria, VA: American Counseling Association.

Kruger, K. A., & Serpell, J. A. (2006). Animal-assisted interventions in mental health: Definitions and theoretical foundations. In A. H. Fine (Ed.), *Handbook on Animal-Assisted Therapy: Theoretical Foundations and Guidelines for Practice* (2nd ed., pp. 21-38). San Diego: Academic Press.

Ladd, G. W., & Ladd, B. K. (1998). Parenting behaviors and parent-child relationships: Correlates of peer victimization in kindergarten? *Developmental Psychology, 34*(6), 1450-1458.

Landreth, G. L. (2002). *Play Therapy: The Art of the Relationship* (2nd ed.). Philadelphia: Brunner-Routledge.

Langbehn, J. (2003). *97 Ways to Make a Dog Smile*. New York: Workman Publishing.

Latner, J. D., & Schwartz, M. B. (2005). Weight bias in a child's world. In K. D. Brownell, R. M. Puhl, M. B. Schwartz, & L. Rudd (Eds.), *Weight Bias: Nature, Consequences, and Remedies* (pp. 54-67). New York: Guilford.

Levinson, B. M., & Mallon, G. P. (1997). *Pet-Oriented Child Psychotherapy* (rev. ed.). Springfield, IL: Charles C. Thomas.

Loar, L., & Colman, L. (2004). *Teaching Empathy: Animal-Assisted Therapy Programs for Children and Families Exposed to Violence*. Alameda, CA: The Latham Foundation.

Ludwig, G. (1996). *Fun and Games With Your Dog*. Hauppauge, NY: Barron's.

Masson, J. M. (1997). *Dogs Never Lie About Love: Reflections on the Emotional Life of Dogs*. New York: Three Rivers Press.

Masson, J. M., & McCarthy, S. (1995). *When Elephants Weep: The Emotional Lives of Animals*. New York: Delta.

McConnell, P. B. (2002). *The Other End of the Leash: Why We Do What We Do Around Dogs*. New York: Ballantine Books.

McConnell, P. B. (2005). *For the Love of a Dog: Understanding Emotion in You and Your Best Friend*. New York: Ballantine Books.

McConnell, P. B. (2006). *For the Love of a Dog: The Biology of Emotion in Two Species* [DVD]. Meridian, ID: Tawzer Dog Videos.

McNicholas, J., & Collis, G. M. (2000). Dogs as catalysts for social interactions: Robustness of the effect. *British Journal of Psychology, 91*, 61-70.

McNicholas, J., & Collis, G. M. (2006). Animals as social supports: Insights for understanding animal-assisted therapy. In A. H. Fine (Ed.), *Handbook on Animal-Assisted Therapy: Theoretical Foundations and Guidelines for Practice* (2nd ed., pp. 49-71). San Diego: Academic Press.

Melson, G. F. (2001). *Why the Wild Things Are: Animals in the Lives of Children.* Cambridge, MA: Harvard University Press.

Messent, P. R. (1983). Social facilitation of contact with other people by pet dogs. In A. H. Katcher & A. M. Beck (Eds.), *New Perspectives on our Lives With Companion Animals* (pp. 37-46). Philadelphia: University of Pennsylvania Press.

Nebbe, L. J. (1997). The human-animal bond's role with the abused child. *Dissertation Abstracts International, Section B: The Sciences and Engineering, 58*(3-B), 1568.

Nimer, J., & Lundahl, B. (2007). Animal-assisted therapy: A meta-analysis. *Anthrozoös, 20*(3), 225-238.

O'Connor, K. J., & Schaefer, C. E. (Eds.). (1994). *Handbook of Play Therapy: Advances and Innovations* (Vol. 2). New York: Wiley.

Overall, K. L. (1997). *Clinical Behavioral Medicine for Small Animals.* St. Louis, MO: Mosby.

Owens, P., & Eckroate, N. (1999). *The Dog Whisperer: A Compassionate, Nonviolent Approach to Dog Training.* Avon, MA: Adams Media Corporation.

Panksepp, J. (2005a). *Affective Neuroscience: The Foundations of Human and Animal Emotions.* New York: Oxford University Press.

Panksepp, J. (2005b). Beyond a joke: From animal laughter to human joy. *Science, 308*, 62.

Pelar, C. (2005). *Living With Kids and Dogs . . . Without Losing Your Mind: A Parent's Guide to Controlling the Chaos.* Woodbridge, VA: C&R Publishing.

Pellegrini, A. D., & Smith, P. K. (Eds.). (2005). *The Nature of Play: Great Apes and Humans.* New York: Guilford.

Podberscek, A. L., Paul, E. S., & Serpell, J. A. (2000). *Companion Animals and Us: Exploring the Relationships Between People and Pets.* New York: Cambridge University Press.

Prothmann, A., Albrecht, K., Dietrich, S., Hornfeck, U., Stieber, S., & Ettrich, C. (2005). Analysis of child-dog play behavior in child psychiatry. *Anthrozoös, 18*(1), 43-58.

Pryor, K. (1999). *Don't Shoot the Dog!: The New Art of Teaching and Training* (rev. ed.). New York: Bantam Books.

Pryor, K. (2005). *Clicker Training for Dogs.* Waltham, MA: Sunshine Books.

Ray, M., & Harding, J. (2005). *Dog Tricks: Fun and Games for Your Clever Canine.* San Diego: Thunder Bay Press.

Reddy, L., Files-Hall, T., & Schaefer, C. E. (Eds.). (2005). *Empirically Based Play Interventions for Children.* Washington, DC: American Psychological Association.

Robinson, S. (2006). Victimization of obese adolescents. *Journal of School Nursing, 22*(4), 201-206.

Rock, M. (1998). *Totally Fun Things to Do With Your Dog.* New York: Wiley.

Rohnke, K. (1991). *The Bottomless Bag.* Dubuque, IA: Kendall/Hunt Publishing.

Rosenthal, L. (1999). *A Dog's Best Friend: An Activity Book for Kids and Their Dogs.* Chicago: Chicago Review Press.

Rugaas, T. (2006). *On Talking Terms With Dogs: Calming Signals* (2nd ed.). Wenatchee, WA: Dogwise Publishing.

Rylant, C. (1995). *Dog Heaven.* New York: Scholastic.

Rylant, C. (1997). *Cat Heaven.* New York: Scholastic.

Sams, M. J., Fortney, E. V., & Willenbring, S. (2006). Occupational therapy incorporating animals for children with autism: A pilot investigation. *American Journal of Occupational Therapy, 60*(3), 268-274.

Schaefer, C. E. (1993). What is play and why is it therapeutic? In C. E. Schaefer (Ed.), *The Therapeutic Powers of Play* (pp. 1-15). Northvale, NJ: Jason Aronson.

Schaefer, C. E., & O'Connor, K. J. (Eds.). (1983). *Handbook of Play Therapy.* New York: Wiley.

Schoen, A. M. (2001). *Kindred Spirits: How the Remarkable Bond Between Humans and Animals Can Change the Way We Live.* New York: Broadway Books.

Sdao, K. (2006). *Know Way, Know How: The Science and Art of Clicker Training* [DVD]. Meridian, ID: Tawzer Dog Videos.

Serpell, J. (Ed.). (1995). *The Domestic Dog: Its Evolution, Behaviour and Interactions With People.* New York: Cambridge University Press.

Serpell, J. A. (1996). *In the Company of Animals* (2nd ed.). New York: Cambridge University Press.

Serpell, J. A. (2000). Creatures of the unconscious: Companion animals as mediators. In A. L. Podberscek, E. S. Paul, & J. A. Serpell (Eds.), *Companion Animals and Us: Exploring the Relationship Between People and Pets* (pp. 108-124). New York: Cambridge University Press.

Shane, F. T. (2006). *Canines in Crisis: Mitigating Traumatic Stress Through Canine Crisis Intervention.* Upper Montclair, NJ: K-9 Disaster Relief Foundation.

Sheppard, C., & Manikoff, J. (1998). *Brave Bart.* Grosse Pointe Woods, MI: Institute for Trauma and Loss in Children.

Silvani, P., & Eckhardt, L. (2005). *Raising Puppies and Kids Together: A Guide for Parents.* Neptune City, NJ: T. F. H. Publications.

Siviy, S. M. (1998). Neurobiological substrates of play behavior: Glimpses into the structure and function of mammalian playfulness. In M. Beckoff & J. A. Byers (Eds.), *Animal Play: Evolutionary, Comparative, and Ecological Perspectives* (pp. 221-242). New York: Cambridge University Press.

Siviy, S. M., Harrison, K. A., & McGregor, I. S. (2006). Fear, risk assessment, and playfulness in the juvenile rat. *Behavioral Neuroscience, 120*(1), 49-59.

Strand, E. B. (2004). Interparental conflict and youth maladjustment: The buffering effects of pets. *Stress, Trauma and Crisis: An International Journal, 7*(3), 151-168.

Sullivan, P. (2006). The healing power of animals. *Healing Magazine, 11*(1), 10-11.

Tellington-Jones, L. (1993). *The Tellington TTouch.* Newark, NJ: Penguin.

Tellington-Jones, L. (2000). *Unleash Your Dog's Potential: Getting in TTouch With Your Canine Friend* [Video]. North Pomfret, VT: Trafalgar Square Publishing.

Tellington-Jones, L. (2001). *Getting in TTouch With Your Dog.* North Pomfret, VT: Trafalgar Square Publishing.

Tellington-Jones, L. (2003). *A TTouch of Magic for Dogs: A Revolutionary Approach to Dog Training* [Video]. Santa Fe, NM: TTEAM & Tellington TTouch Training.

Terr, L. (1990). *Too Scared to Cry: How Trauma Affects Children . . . and Ultimately Us All.* New York: Basic Books.

Thomas, E. M. (1993). *The Hidden Life of Dogs.* New York: Pocket Books.

Thompson, M. J. (2007). *Effects of a Trained Therapy Dog in Child-Centered Play Therapy on Children With Anxiety Disorders.* Unpublished doctoral dissertation proposal, Argosy University, Sarasota, FL.

VanFleet, R. (1993). Strengthening families with storytelling. In L. VandeCreek, S. Knapp, & T. L. Jackson (Eds.), *Innovations in Clinical Practice: A Source Book* (Vol. 12, pp. 147-154). Sarasota, FL: Professional Resource Press.

VanFleet, R. (1997). Play and perfectionism: Putting fun back into families. In H. G. Kaduson, D. Cangelosi, & C. E. Schaefer (Eds.), *The Playing Cure: Individualized Play Therapy for Specific Childhood Problems* (pp. 61-82). Northvale, NJ: Jason Aronson.

VanFleet, R. (2004). *It's Only Natural: Exploring the Play in Play Therapy Workshop Manual.* Boiling Springs, PA: Play Therapy Press.

VanFleet, R. (2005). *Filial Therapy: Strengthening Parent-Child Relationships Through Play* (2nd ed.). Sarasota, FL: Professional Resource Press.

VanFleet, R. (2006a). *Child-Centered Play Therapy* [DVD workshop]. Boiling Springs, PA: Play Therapy Press.

VanFleet, R. (2006b). *The Faces of Play: A Photographic Exploration of the Importance and Joys of Playfulness.* Boiling Springs, PA: Play Therapy Press.

VanFleet, R. (2007a). *Pet Play Therapy: A Workshop Manual.* Boiling Springs, PA: Play Therapy Press.

VanFleet, R. (2007b). *Preliminary Results From the Ongoing Pet Play Therapy Study.* Boiling Springs, PA: Play Therapy Press (www.play-therapy.com/pets_study.html or www.playful pooch.org).

VanFleet, R. (2008). Playful pooches: Using canine interactions to enhance therapeutic outcomes for children and adolescents. In

C. F. Sori & L. Hecker (Eds.), *The Therapist's Notebook III: More Homework, Handouts & Activities for Use in Psychotherapy*. New York: Haworth Press.

VanFleet, R., Ryan, S. D., & Smith, S. K. (2005). Filial therapy: A critical review. In L. Reddy, T. Files-Hall, & C. E. Schaefer (Eds.), *Empirically Based Play Interventions for Children* (pp. 241-264). Washington, DC: American Psychological Association.

VanFleet, R., & Sniscak, C. C. (2003). Filial Therapy for attachment-disrupted and disordered children. In R. VanFleet & L. Guerney (Eds.), *Casebook of Filial Therapy* (pp. 279-308). Boiling Springs, PA: Play Therapy Press.

Webb, N. B. (Ed.). (1999). *Play Therapy for Children in Crisis: Individual, Group, and Family Treatment* (2nd ed.). New York: Guilford.

Wells, M. J. (1998). The effect of pets on children's stress responses during medical procedures. *Dissertation Abstracts International, Section B: The Sciences and Engineering, 59*(6-B), 2689.

Weston, R., & Ross, C. (2005). *Kids & Dogs: Teaching Them to Live, Play, and Learn Together*. Crow's Nest, New South Wales, Australia: Allen & Unwin.

Wilson, K., & Ryan, V. (2005). *Play Therapy: A Nondirective Approach for Children and Adolescents* (2nd ed.). Philadelphia: Elsevier.

Woolley, C. C. (2005). Changes in child symptomatology associated with animal-assisted therapy. *Dissertation Abstracts International; Section B: The Sciences and Engineering, 65*(12-B), 6681.

**For more information about play therapy,
visit the author's website:**

www.play-therapy.com

**For more information about animals in
play therapy, visit Risë's other website:**

www.playfulpooch.org

Or contact Dr. VanFleet directly:

Risë VanFleet, PhD
Family Enhancement & Play Therapy Center, Inc.
PO Box 613
Boiling Springs, PA 17007
USA

717-249-4707
Risevanfleet@aol.com

Consider joining the International Collaborative on Play
Therapy, an online community of people interested in
play and play therapy. Membership is free. For
information or to join, go to www.play-therapy.com,
then click on International.

If You Found This Book Useful . . .

You might want to know more about our other titles.

If you would like to receive our latest catalog, please return this form:

Name: _____
(Please Print)

Address: _____

Address: _____

City/State/Zip: _____
This is ☐ home ☐ office

Telephone: (_____)_____

E-mail: _____

Fax: (_____) _____

I am a:

☐ Psychologist   ☐ Marriage and Family Therapist
☐ Clinical Social Worker   ☐ Not in Mental Health Field
☐ Mental Health Counselor   ☐ Other: _____

◆   ◆   ◆

Professional Resource Press
P.O. Box 3197
Sarasota, FL 34230-3197

Telephone: 800-443-3364
FAX: 941-343-9201
E-mail: cs.prpress@gmail.com
Website: www.prpress.com

PTK/7/12

Add A Colleague To Our Mailing List . . .

If you would like us to send our latest catalog to one of your colleagues, please return this form:

Name: _____
(Please Print)

Address: _____

Address: _____

City/State/Zip: _____
This is ▢ home ▢ office

Telephone: (_____)_____

E-mail: _____

Fax: (_____) _____

This person is a:

▢ Psychologist   ▢ Marriage and Family Therapist
▢ Clinical Social Worker   ▢ Not in Mental Health Field
▢ Mental Health Counselor   ▢ Other: _____

Name of person completing this form: _____

◆ ◆ ◆

Professional Resource Press
P.O. Box 3197
Sarasota, FL 34230-3197

Telephone: 800-443-3364
FAX: 941-343-9201
E-mail: cs.prpress@gmail.com
Website: www.prpress.com